My Spelling Workbook

Prim-Ed
Publishing

My Spelling Workbook – Book B
© R.I.C. Publications

Offices in: United Kingdom: PO Box 2840, Coventry, CV6 5ZY
Australia: PO Box 332, Greenwood, Western Australia 6924
Republic of Ireland: Bosheen, New Ross, Co. Wexford, Ireland

First Published in 1990, R.I.C. Publications
Revised and Reprinted 2001, Prim-Ed Publishing
ISBN 1 86400 634 X

Introduction

Welcome to My Spelling Workbook. This book has lots of different activities to help you improve your spelling. Here are some tips to show you the best way to use your book.

- ## Learning Words

  Each list of words in the book has five test columns. Every time you spell a word correctly in a test, you can tick the column.

  Three ticks in a row shows that you know how to spell the word.

  If you do not get three ticks in a row, you write 'T' in the transfer box. When you start your next list of words, you add the word to the table 'Difficult Words I Have Found'. You can also add any other difficult words you find.

- ## Look, Say, Trace, Cover, Write, Check

  These words are to remind you of the best way to learn to spell.
  You should follow this when you are learning each word.

- ## Recording your Scores

  At the back of the book, you will find a grid for recording your scores for each unit. This will help you to keep track of how you are improving with your spelling.

- ## How to Become a Better Speller

  1. *Have a go!*
     Write the word on the piece of paper.
     Does it look right? If it doesn't look right, try writing it another way.
  2. *Look around your classroom*
     There are probably many words around you that you just didn't notice.
  3. *Use a dictionary*
     Try using a dictionary before you ask a teacher.
  4. *Ask the teacher*
     If you have tried the first three, then ask a teacher for help.

Contents

List Words	Test 1	Test 2	Test 3	Test 4	Test 5	T
end						
send						
bend						
mend						
lend						
spend						
grow						
slow						
show						
bump						
jump						
lump						
pump						
camp						
stamp						

Look   Say   Trace   Cover   Write   Check

Difficult Words I Have Found	Test 1	Test 2	Test 3	T

Picture Matching

1. Write the list word that matches each picture.

(a)

_____

(b)

_____

(c)

_____

What am I?

2. I am long and thin.
   I can be used on tyres and balls.
   I fill things with air.

   I am a _____.

3. Use list words to solve the crossword.

across

4. Hop, skip and _____

5. Put on a letter

6. A bicycle _____

7. Same as finish

9. Opposite of fast

10. Similar to curve

12. To get bigger

13. Can you _____ me some money?

down

1. Do not _____ people when they are writing

2. There were seven tents in the _____

3. A _____ of clay

5. Opposite of save

8. To fix

9. _____ me your work

11. Did your mother _____ a note?

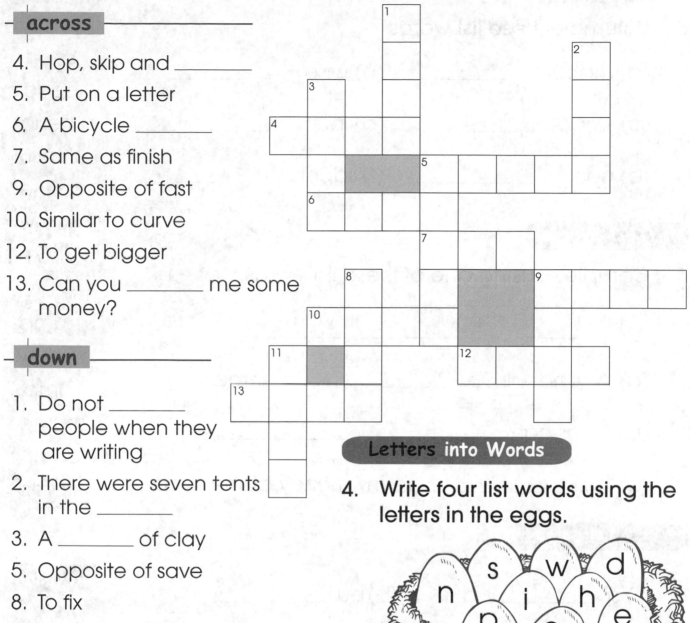

Letters into Words

4. Write four list words using the letters in the eggs.

_____

_____

_____

_____

Additional Activities

- Write the list words using look, say, trace, cover, write, check.
- Write five more 'amp' words. Check your spelling.
- Find small words in the list words.

 **UNIT 1**

All Mixed Up

5. Unjumble these list words.

(a) mpbu _____ (b) wlso _____

(c) smpat _____ (d) lpum _____

(e) nde _____ (f) sdpen _____

Missing Words

6. Complete, using one of these list words.

| jump | spend | grow |

(a) A seed will _____ into a tree.

(b) Frogs can _____.

(c) I will _____ my money at the shop.

Missing Letters

7. (a) sp_____ _____d (b) pu _____ _____

(c) m_____ _____d (d) be _____ _____

Read and Draw

8.
(a) A bump on my head.	(b) A rabbit can jump.

List

end
send
bend
mend
lend
spend
grow
slow
show
bump
jump
lump
pump
camp
stamp

Revision

fox
his
cup
can
bad
the
my
deep
moon
one

9. **Find these list words in the word search.**

send	lump	grow
camp	pump	slow
stamp	lend	show
end	bend	bump
spend	mend	jump

j	s	l	s	b	u	m	p	a
u	t	u	e	s	k	b	u	s
m	a	m	t	l	c	a	m	p
p	m	p	b	o	l	s	p	e
o	p	s	e	w	e	h	x	n
w	l	f	n	t	n	o	u	d
m	e	n	d	i	d	w	r	t
s	h	s	e	n	d	r	r	y
g	r	o	w	m	k	e	n	d

Spelling Sums

10. (a) b + ump = bump

    (b) l + ook = _____

    (c) j + ump = _____

    (d) sp + end = _____

    (e) s + end =

    (f) sh + ow = _____

Word Worm

11. Circle each list word you can find in the word worm.

s l o w e n d j u m p
c o w o h s p m u b
a c w o h s p m u b
a m p m e n d b e n d

Memory Master

12. Cover the list words. Write two from memory.

    _____   _____

    Write a sentence using both words.

    _____

    _____

    _____

    _____

List Words	Test 1	Test 2	Test 3	Test 4	Test 5	T
go						
so						
flag						
glad						
slip						
swim						
pram						
drum						
drop						
drip						
spot						
from						
help						
left						
out						

Look   Say   Trace   Cover   Write   Check

Difficult Words I Have Found	Test 1	Test 2	Test 3	T

Word Hunt

1. (a) Which list words end in 't'?

   _____

   _____

   _____

   (b) Which list word rhymes with dam?

   _____

   (c) Write the list word that has three letters.

   _____

   (d) Write the list word that means the same as 'happy'.

   _____

2. Use list words to solve the crossword.

across

1. Rhymes with go
4. You bang it
5. Opposite of in
6. Opposite of right
8. Happy
10. Don't _____ on the banana
11. Same as start
12. You push a baby in it

down

1. A dot
2. Where did you come _____?
3. A police officer will _____ you
7. Found at the top of a flagpole
9. To let something fall
10. Done in the water

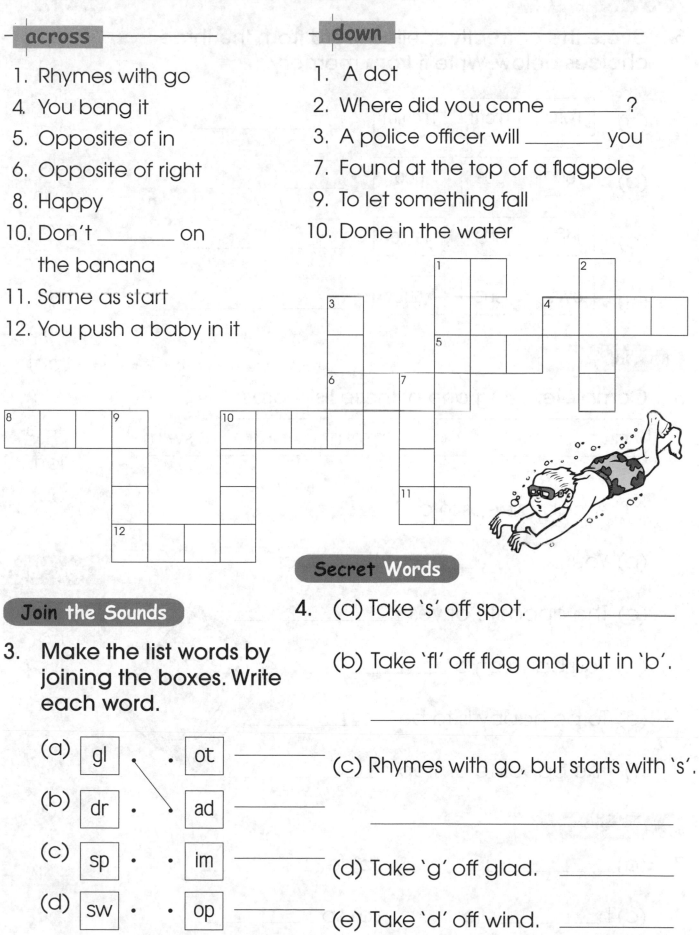

Secret Words

4. (a) Take 's' off spot. _____

(b) Take 'fl' off flag and put in 'b'.

_____

(c) Rhymes with go, but starts with 's'.

_____

(d) Take 'g' off glad. _____

(e) Take 'd' off wind. _____

Join the Sounds

3. Make the list words by joining the boxes. Write each word.

(a) gl • • ot _____

(b) dr • • ad _____

(c) sp • • im _____

(d) sw • • op _____

Memory Master

5. Circle the correctly spelled word from the three choices below. Write it from memory.

(a) | fom | from | fromm | _____

(b) | go | goe | goo | _____

(c) | left | leftt | lefte | _____

(d) | owt | out | aut | _____

List

go
so
flag
glad
slip
swim
pram
drum
drop
drip
spot
from
help
left
out

Missing Words

6. Complete, using one of these list words.

> go   glad   no   pram   drum   swim

(a) A baby sleeps in a _____.

(b) You _____ at the beach

(c) The opposite of yes is _____.

(d) You bang on a _____.

(e) To be happy is to be _____.

(f) The opposite of stop is _____.

Revision

ran
hot
dad
am
bag
get
mix
is
sun
jug

Missing Letters

7. (a) _____ _____ip   (b) le _____ _____

(c) h_____ _____p   (d) sp _____ _____

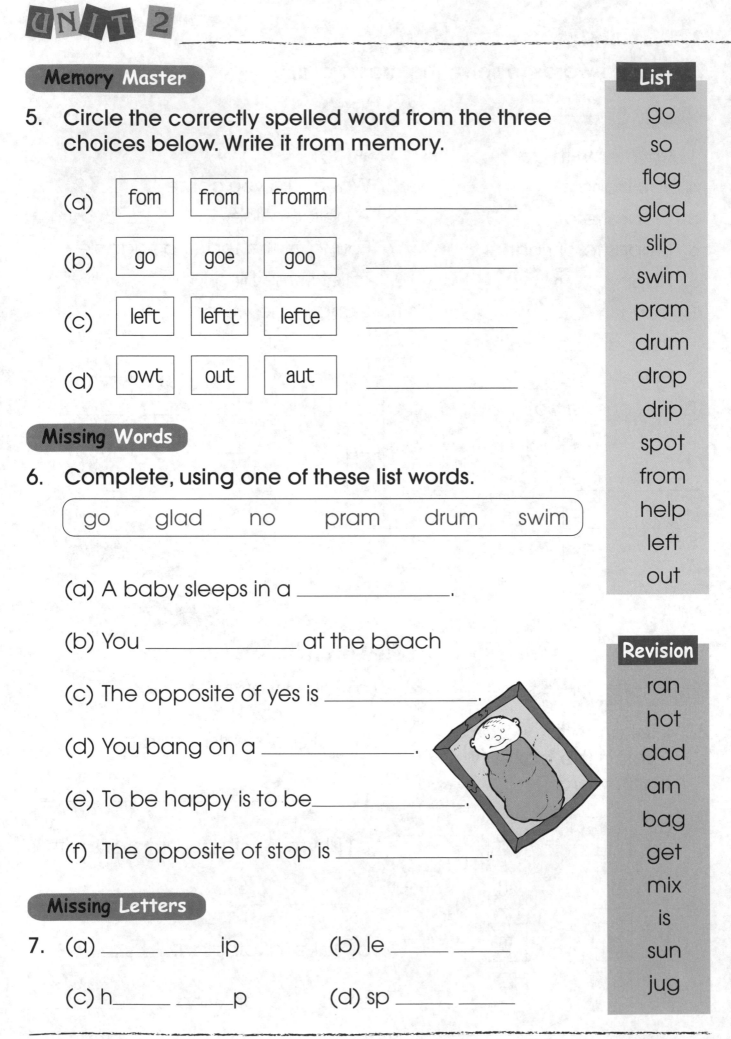

8. **Find these list words in the word search.**

go   out   so

from   drip   drop

glad   spot   flag

drum   pram   help

swim   left   slip

u	z	t	t	g	l	a	d	z
q	f	d	r	o	p	w	y	s
j	r	w	x	k	s	x	f	p
s	o	p	h	l	w	z	g	o
v	m	r	e	w	i	n	d	t
d	e	a	l	k	m	z	r	f
r	e	m	p	u	v	o	u	l
i	l	e	f	t	v	u	m	a
p	f	s	l	i	p	t	q	g

Picture Matching

9. **Look at the each picture. Circle the correct word. Write it on the line.**

(a)
drum, drums

_____

(b)
pram, prams

_____

(c)
spot, spots

_____

Shape Sorter

10. **Write a word that fits in each shape.**

go swim left spot pram drip

(a)

(b)

(c)

(d)

(e)

(f)

UNIT 3

List Words	Test 1	Test 2	Test 3	Test 4	Test 5	T
add						
and						
land						
sand						
hand						
band						
duck						
truck						
rock						
clock						
neck						
black						
sick						
lick						
sock						

Look   Say   Trace   Cover   Write   Check

Difficult Words I Have Found	Test 1	Test 2	Test 3	T

Word Worm

1. Circle each list word you can find in the word worm.

sickandducksockbandtruckrockland

Word Maker

2. How many words can you make?

ha

ba

nd

sa

a

la

_____

_____

_____

_____

3. Use list words to solve the crossword.

across

2. Shows the time
5. One _____ one is two
7. To join one thing to another
8. Plays music
9. Carries heavy things
12. Not well
13. You put it on your foot

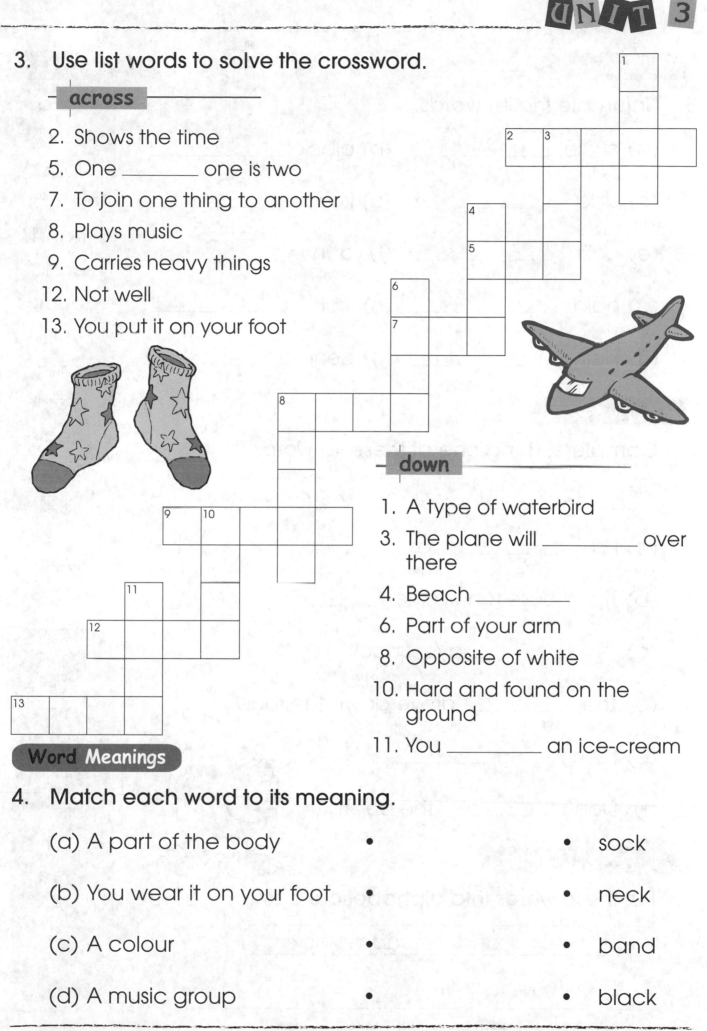

down

1. A type of waterbird
3. The plane will _____ over there
4. Beach _____
6. Part of your arm
8. Opposite of white
10. Hard and found on the ground
11. You _____ an ice-cream

Word Meanings

4. Match each word to its meaning.

(a) A part of the body • • sock

(b) You wear it on your foot • • neck

(c) A colour • • band

(d) A music group • • black

All Mixed Up

5. Unjumble the list words.

(a) ckclo _____ (b) albck _____

(c) dda _____ (d) kucd _____

(e) cokr _____ (f) dan _____

(g) nald _____ (h) ikcl _____

(i) kics _____ (j) cenk _____

Missing Words

6. Complete, using one of these list words.

sick   rock   truck   and   duck   clock

(a) Fish _____ chips.

(b) The mouse ran up the _____.

(c) A _____ says 'quack'.

(d) The _____ drove down the road.

(e) I am feeling _____.

(f) Don't _____ the boat!

Alphabetical Order

7. Put these words into alphabetical order.

lick   rock   and   hand   black

List

add
and
land
sand
hand
band
duck
truck
rock
clock
neck
black
sick
lick
sock

Revision

an
tin
pig
lip
sat
hit
met
gap
of
hen

8. Find these list words in the word search.

and rock land

clock sand neck

add   black hand

sick   band lick

duck   sock truck

p	l	a	n	d	z	u	x	s
d	u	c	k	r	o	c	k	t
l	f	s	g	b	y	q	j	a
t	v	a	v	l	h	s	l	d
r	q	n	f	a	a	s	i	d
u	y	d	j	c	n	e	c	k
c	l	o	c	k	d	k	k	h
k	a	n	d	a	s	o	c	k
s	i	c	k	b	a	n	d	h

Riddles

9. The answers to these riddles rhyme with 'and'

(a) I am part of your body and have five fingers.

  I am a _____.

(b) I am found on the ground and can be different colours. Children like playing with me.

  I am _____.

Fill in the Gap

10. (a) stand

  stan___

  sta ___ ___

  st___ ___ ___

  s___ ___ ___ ___

  _____

(b) black

  blac___

  bla___ ___

  bl___ ___ ___

  b___ ___ ___ ___

  _____

(c) neck

  nec___

  ne___ ___

  n ___ ___ ___

  _____

List Words	Test 1	Test 2	Test 3	Test 4	Test 5	T
pest						
rest						
best						
must						
lost						
cost						
nest						
stop						
stand						
wool						
wood						
good						
day						
week						
year						

Look Say Trace Cover Write Check

Difficult Words I Have Found	Test 1	Test 2	Test 3	T

Letters into Words

1. Write four list words using the letters in the logs.

s
t
e
p
r
o
i
c

(a) _____

(b) _____

(c) _____

(d) _____

What am I?

2. I keep you warm.

   You can knit with me.

   I come from sheep.

   I am _____.

3. Use list words to solve the crossword.

across

3. The trunk of a tree is made of _____
5. 52 weeks in one _____
7. Opposite of sit
9. The price of something
10. 7 days in one _____
12. Opposite of worst
13. A fly is a _____

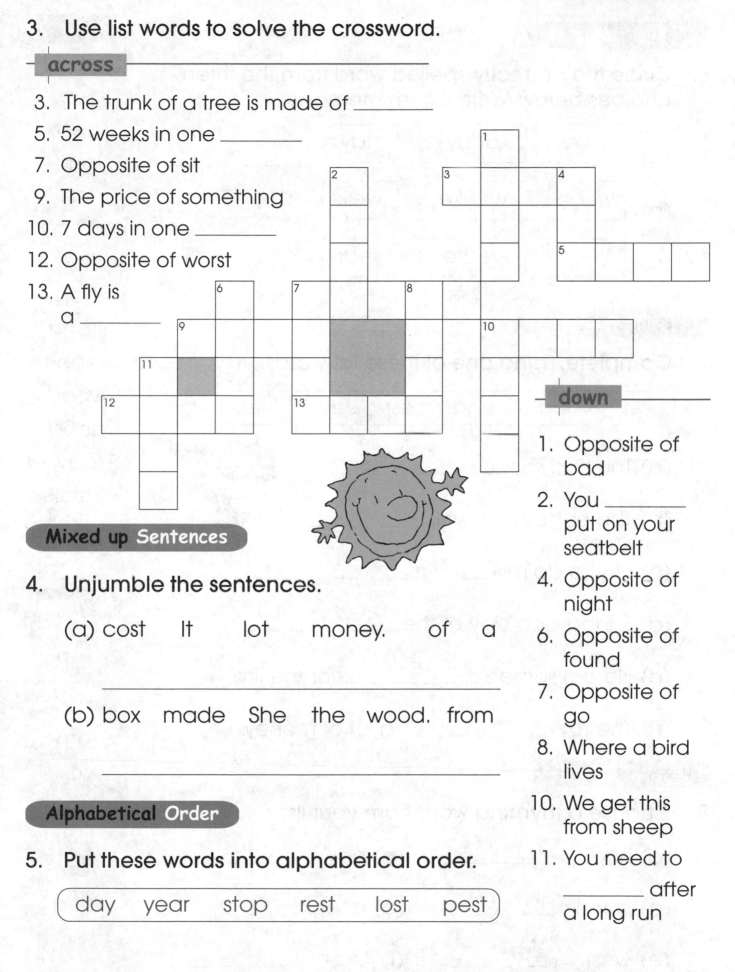

down

1. Opposite of bad
2. You _____ put on your seatbelt
4. Opposite of night
6. Opposite of found
7. Opposite of go
8. Where a bird lives
10. We get this from sheep
11. You need to _____ after a long run

Mixed up Sentences

4. Unjumble the sentences.

(a) cost   It   lot   money.   of   a

_____

(b) box   made   She   the   wood.   from

_____

Alphabetical Order

5. Put these words into alphabetical order.

    day   year   stop   rest   lost   pest

UNIT 4

Memory Master

6. Circle the correctly spelled word from the three choices below. Write it from memory.

(a) | daye | dauy | day | _____

(b) | week | weeke | weik | _____

(c) | yeer | yeare | year | _____

Missing Words

7. Complete, using one of these list words:

nest   wood   stand   cost   best   week

(a) The bird made a _____.

(b) The opposite of sit is _____.

(c) I try to do my _____.

(d) Sunday is a day of the _____.

(e) He got some _____ for the fire.

(f) The toy _____ a lot of money.

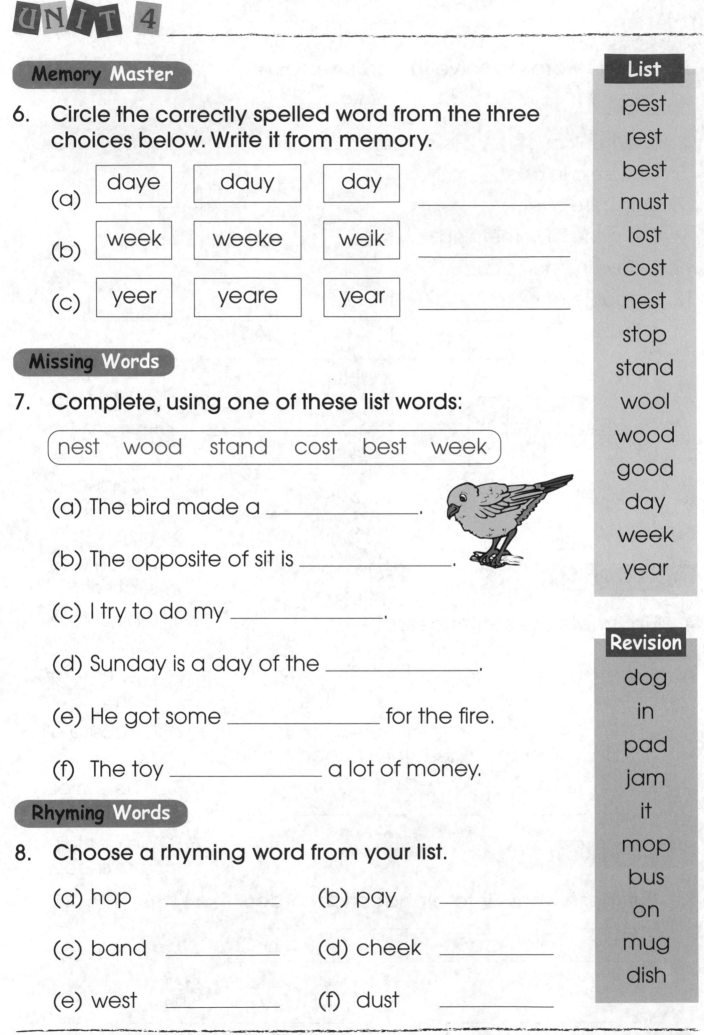

Rhyming Words

8. Choose a rhyming word from your list.

(a) hop _____   (b) pay _____

(c) band _____   (d) cheek _____

(e) west _____   (f) dust _____

List

pest
rest
best
must
lost
cost
nest
stop
stand
wool
wood
good
day
week
year

Revision

dog
in
pad
jam
it
mop
bus
on
mug
dish

9. **Find these list words in the word search.**

day	rest
week	lost
year	nest
wool	best
wood	must
good	cost
pest	stop
stand	

d	r	w	m	c	w	i	s	w
a	e	o	u	o	a	n	t	o
y	s	o	s	s	s	t	a	o
g	t	d	t	t	y	o	n	l
o	o	y	e	a	r	z	d	o
o	r	n	o	o	s	t	o	p
d	z	e	r	b	e	s	t	l
l	o	s	t	m	p	e	s	t
b	e	t	m	k	w	e	e	k

Memory Master

10. (a) Cover the list words. Write two from memory.

_____   _____

(b) Write a sentence using both words.

_____

Missing Words

11. **Write the correct list or revision word.**

(a) Write the revision words that have 'o' in them.

_____ _____ _____

(b) Write two words that rhyme with 'test'.

_____ _____

(c) Write the list word that means the same as 'price'.

_____

(d) Write the word that is the opposite of bad.

_____

List Words	Test 1	Test 2	Test 3	Test 4	Test 5	T
ant						
disk						
milk						
desk						
pole						
hole						
mole						
sole						
shut						
shed						
shot						
sheep						
smash						
crush						
brush						

Look   Say   Trace   Cover   Write   Check

Difficult Words I Have Found	Test 1	Test 2	Test 3	T

Word Hunt

1. (a) Which list words end in 't'?

   _____

   _____

   _____

   (b) Write the list word that rhymes with 'hot'.

   _____

   (c) Write the list word that has three letters.

   _____

What am I?

2. I am white.

   I come from a cow.

   You drink me.

   I am _____.

3. Use list words to solve the crossword.

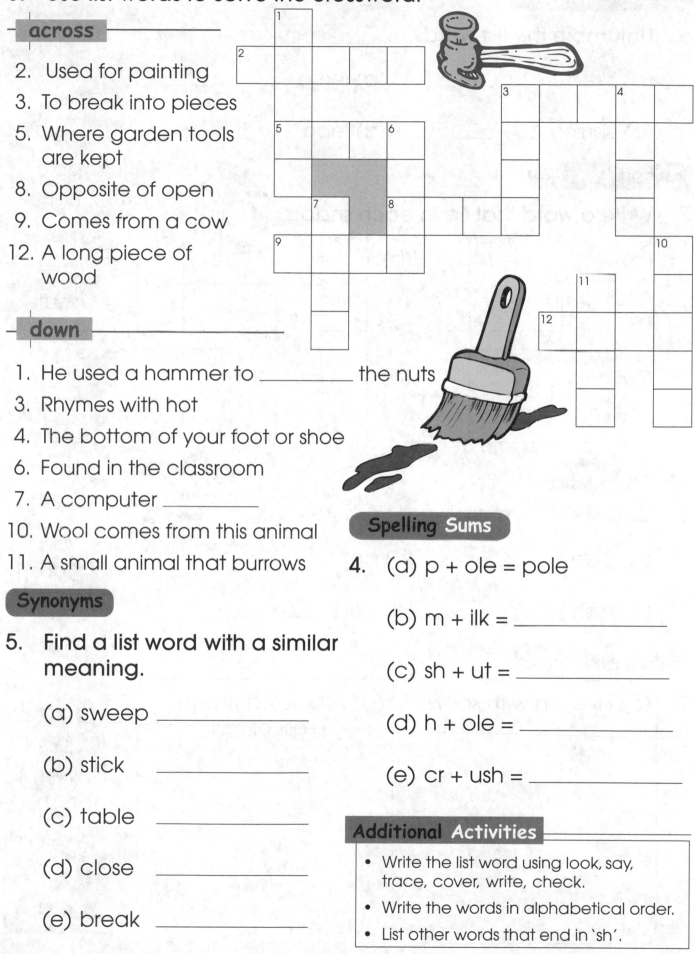

across

2. Used for painting
3. To break into pieces
5. Where garden tools are kept
8. Opposite of open
9. Comes from a cow
12. A long piece of wood

down

1. He used a hammer to _____ the nuts
3. Rhymes with hot
4. The bottom of your foot or shoe
6. Found in the classroom
7. A computer _____
10. Wool comes from this animal
11. A small animal that burrows

Synonyms

5. Find a list word with a similar meaning.

   (a) sweep _____

   (b) stick _____

   (c) table _____

   (d) close _____

   (e) break _____

Spelling Sums

4. (a) p + ole = pole

   (b) m + ilk = _____

   (c) sh + ut = _____

   (d) h + ole = _____

   (e) cr + ush = _____

Additional Activities

- Write the list word using look, say, trace, cover, write, check.
- Write the words in alphabetical order.
- List other words that end in 'sh'.

UNIT 5

Memory Master

6. Unjumble the list words.

    (a) sked _____   (b) lemo _____

    (c) shmsa _____   (d) lepo _____

Missing Words

7. Write a word that fits in each shape.

    (a)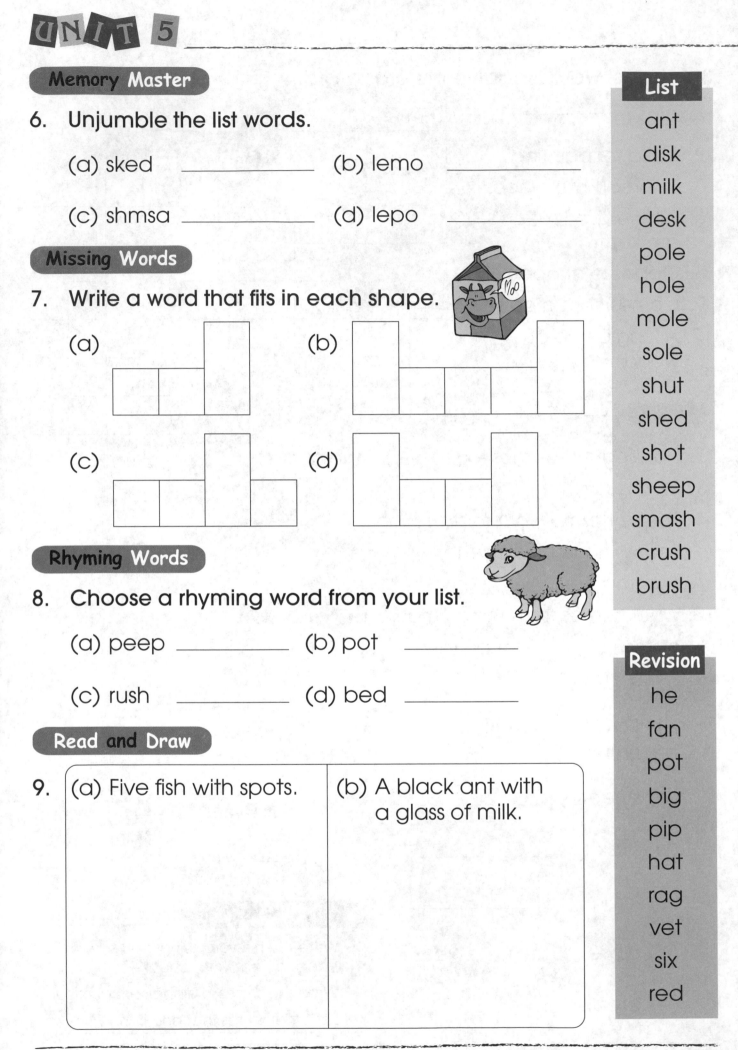

    (b)

    (c)

    (d)

Rhyming Words

8. Choose a rhyming word from your list.

    (a) peep _____   (b) pot _____

    (c) rush _____   (d) bed _____

Read and Draw

9. | (a) Five fish with spots. | (b) A black ant with a glass of milk. |
    |---|---|
    | | |

List

ant
disk
milk
desk
pole
hole
mole
sole
shut
shed
shot
sheep
smash
crush
brush

Revision

he
fan
pot
big
pip
hat
rag
vet
six
red

10. **Find these list words in the word search.**

ant	shut
plant	shed
milk	shot
desk	sheep
pole	smash
hole	crush
mole	brush
sole	

d	p	z	z	s	o	l	e	p
i	o	s	j	h	s	w	m	l
s	l	h	l	e	h	b	o	a
m	e	u	g	d	o	r	l	n
a	n	t	m	p	t	u	e	t
s	g	w	i	s	h	s	s	d
h	h	o	l	e	g	h	h	k
d	e	s	k	c	r	u	s	h
s	h	e	e	p	u	o	e	o

Small Words

11. **Find a small word in these words.**

    (a) crush _____

    (b) shot _____

    (c) shut _____

    (d) smash _____

    (e) ant _____

    (f) shed _____

Word Maker

12. **How many words can you make?**

_____

_____

_____

_____

_____

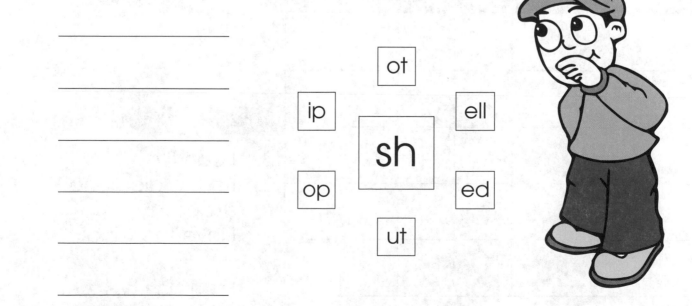

ot

ip   **sh**   ell

op   ed

ut

UNIT 6

List Words	Test 1	Test 2	Test 3	Test 4	Test 5	T
kite						
drive						
side						
nine						
five						
ride						
like						
line						
hide						
went						
dent						
bent						
tent						
sent						
lent						

Look   Say   Trace   Cover   Write   Check

Difficult Words I Have Found	Test 1	Test 2	Test 3	T

Picture Matching

1. Write the list word that matches each picture.

(a)

_____

(b)

_____

(c)

_____

What am I?

2. I can fly.
   I am a diamond shape.
   I love the wind.

   I am a _____.

3. Use list words to solve the crossword.

across

4. Comes before 10
5. Who _____ the letter?
7. You _____ a horse
8. Opposite to borrowed
10. Opposite to dislike
13. Used when camping
14. You _____ a car.

down

1. Having a curve
2. Comes after four
3. The car had a _____ in the door.
6. _____ and seek
8. Can you draw a _____?
9. She _____ to the shops
11. Flown in the sky
12. Which _____ are you on?

Word Worm

4. Circle each list word you can find in the word worm.

Small Words

5. Find a small word in these list words.

(a) ride _____

(b) nine _____

(c) dent _____

(d) tent _____

Additional Activities

- Write the list words using look, say, trace, cover, write, check.
- Write 5 more 'i–e' words. Check spelling
- Write the list words in alphabetical order

Word Meanings

6. **Match each word to its meaning.**

   (a) hide • • something you take camping

   (b) tent • • it flies in the sky

   (c) five • • to not be seen

   (d) kite • • a number

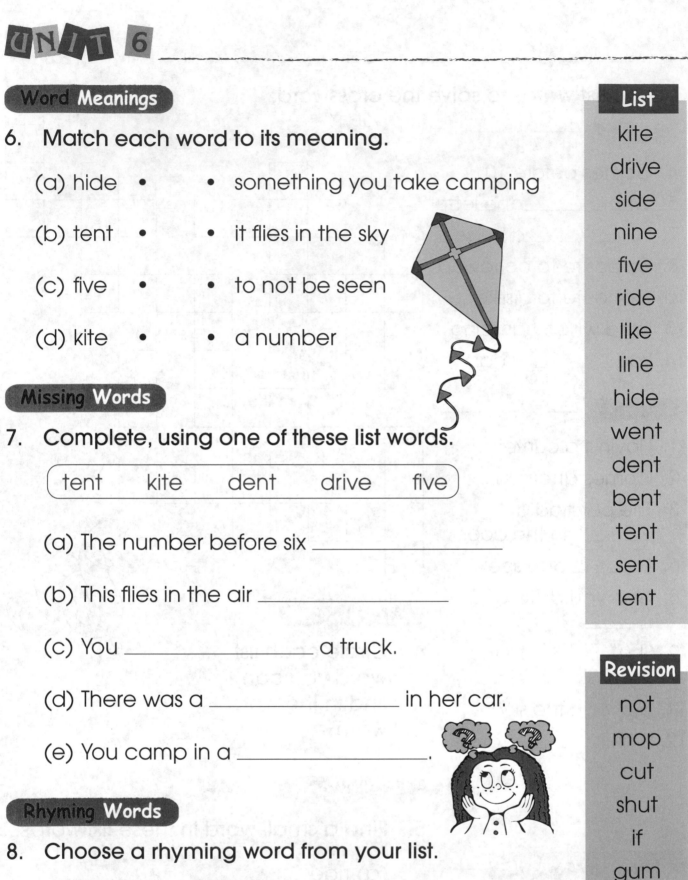

Missing Words

7. **Complete, using one of these list words.**

   | tent | kite | dent | drive | five |

   (a) The number before six _____

   (b) This flies in the air _____

   (c) You _____ a truck.

   (d) There was a _____ in her car.

   (e) You camp in a _____.

Rhyming Words

8. **Choose a rhyming word from your list.**

   (a) hive _____ (b) bite _____

   (c) tide _____ (d) cent _____

   (e) fine _____ (f) bike _____

List

kite
drive
side
nine
five
ride
like
line
hide
went
dent
bent
tent
sent
lent

Revision

not
mop
cut
shut
if
gum
as
feet
cow
no

9. **Find these list words in the word search.**

kite   lent

drive   went

side   dent

nine   bent

five   tent

ride   sent

like   line

hide

n	i	n	e	q	u	z	k	q
c	h	s	d	e	n	t	i	b
x	i	g	c	x	l	i	t	e
u	d	l	q	f	i	v	e	n
d	e	e	w	p	k	j	s	t
r	z	n	e	s	e	u	e	p
i	g	t	n	i	t	e	n	t
v	x	q	t	d	i	c	t	j
e	r	i	d	e	l	i	n	e

Word Hunt

10. (a) Find the list words beginning with 'l'.

_____ _____

_____

(b) Which list words are numbers?

_____ _____

(c) Which list words rhyme with wide?

_____ _____

_____

(d) Which list words rhyme with hive?

_____ _____

Memory Master

11. **Cover the list words.**

Write two from memory.

_____

_____

Write a sentence using both words.

_____

_____

UNIT 7

List Words	Test 1	Test 2	Test 3	Test 4	Test 5	T
hill						
fill						
still						
mill						
till						
will						
been						
tree						
green						
sweep						
sleep						
street						
here						
they						
have						

Look   Say   Trace   Cover   Write   Check

Difficult Words I Have Found	Test 1	Test 2	Test 3	T

Letters into Words

1. Write four list words using the letters in the apples.

   (a) _____

   (b) _____

   (c) _____

   (d) _____

Small Words

2. Find small words in these list words.

   (a) been

   _____

   (b) here

   _____

   (c) they

   _____

3. Use list words to solve the crossword.

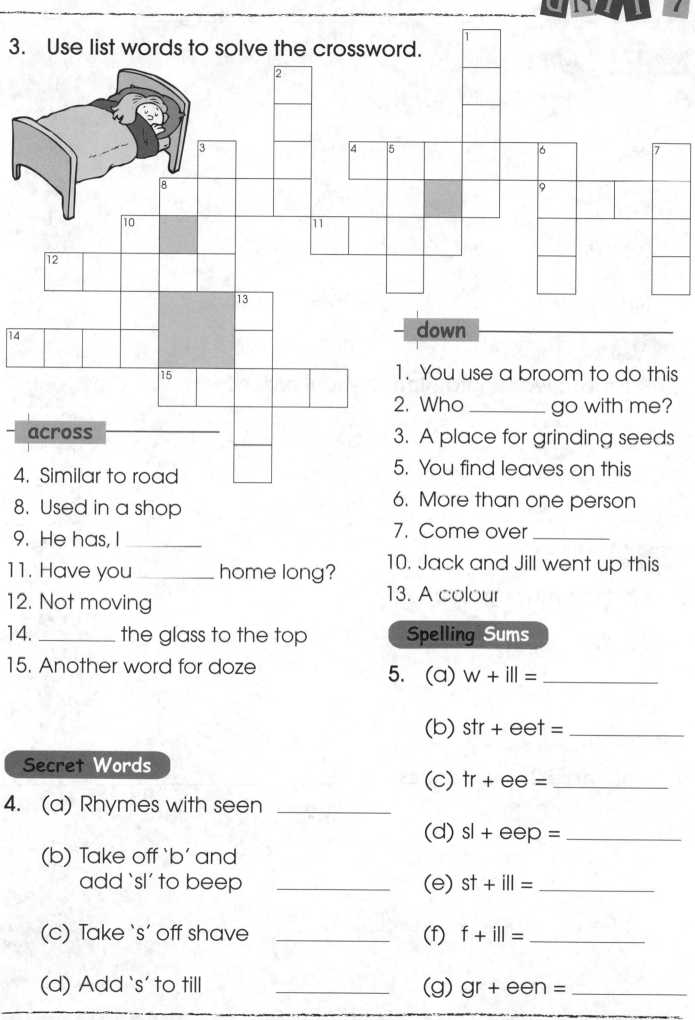

across

4. Similar to road
8. Used in a shop
9. He has, I _____
11. Have you _____ home long?
12. Not moving
14. _____ the glass to the top
15. Another word for doze

down

1. You use a broom to do this
2. Who _____ go with me?
3. A place for grinding seeds
5. You find leaves on this
6. More than one person
7. Come over _____
10. Jack and Jill went up this
13. A colour

Secret Words

4. (a) Rhymes with seen _____

   (b) Take off 'b' and
       add 'sl' to beep _____

   (c) Take 's' off shave _____

   (d) Add 's' to till _____

Spelling Sums

5. (a) w + ill = _____

   (b) str + eet = _____

   (c) tr + ee = _____

   (d) sl + eep = _____

   (e) st + ill = _____

   (f) f + ill = _____

   (g) gr + een = _____

All Mixed Up

6. Unjumble these list words.

(a) itll _____   (b) enbe _____

(c) hree _____   (d) liml _____

(e) tills _____   (f) yteh _____

(g) nerge _____   (h) rete _____

Additional Activities

7. Put these words into alphabetical order.

┌───┐
│ mill   been   they   tree   fill   green   │
└───┘

_____

Missing Letters

8. Find the missing letters.

(a) sw___ ___p (b) s___ ___ ___p (c) w___l___

(d) st___ ee___ (e) hi___ ___ (f) ___r___en

Mixed up Sentences

9. Unjumble the sentences.

(a) hill.   up   Run   the

_____

(b) Here   the   street!   is

_____

List

hill
fill
still
mill
till
will
been
tree
green
sweep
sleep
street
here
they
have

Revision

bin
wig
bat
sit
let
but
rug
has
feed
food

10. **Find these list words in the word search.**

hill	tree
fill	here
still	green
mill	sweep
till	sleep
will	street
have	they
been	

d	g	w	i	l	l	s	h	t
o	r	k	s	s	e	p	i	i
h	e	r	e	t	n	t	l	l
a	e	g	p	r	m	i	l	l
v	n	t	g	e	s	b	q	s
e	h	h	e	e	w	e	f	l
t	r	e	e	t	e	e	i	e
y	x	y	q	c	e	n	l	e
s	t	i	l	l	p	e	l	p

Correct Words

11. **Circle the correct word.**

    (a) There is one tree/trees.   (b) The hill/hills is very high.

    (c) I have two feet/feets.

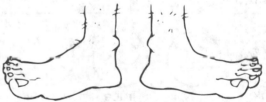

Rhyming Words

12. (a) Find all the list words that rhyme.

hill	deep	see
_____	_____	_____
_____	_____	
_____		
_____		

	been	feet
	_____	_____

    (b) Which list words don't rhyme with any of these?

    _____

UNIT 8

List Words	Test 1	Test 2	Test 3	Test 4	Test 5	T
bell						
sell						
well						
fell						
tell						
spell						
doll						
thing						
swing						
sing						
bring						
long						
bang						
sang						
hang						

Look Say Trace Cover Write Check

Difficult Words I Have Found	Test 1	Test 2	Test 3	T

What am I?

1. (a) I am made from metal.

   You can ring me.

   I make sound.

   I am a _____.

   (b) I am filled with water.

   I am made from bricks.

   You can make a wish if you throw a coin into me.

   I am a _____.

   (c) I have a seat.

   I live in a playground.

   I go backwards and forwards.

   I am a _____.

2. Use list words to solve the crossword.

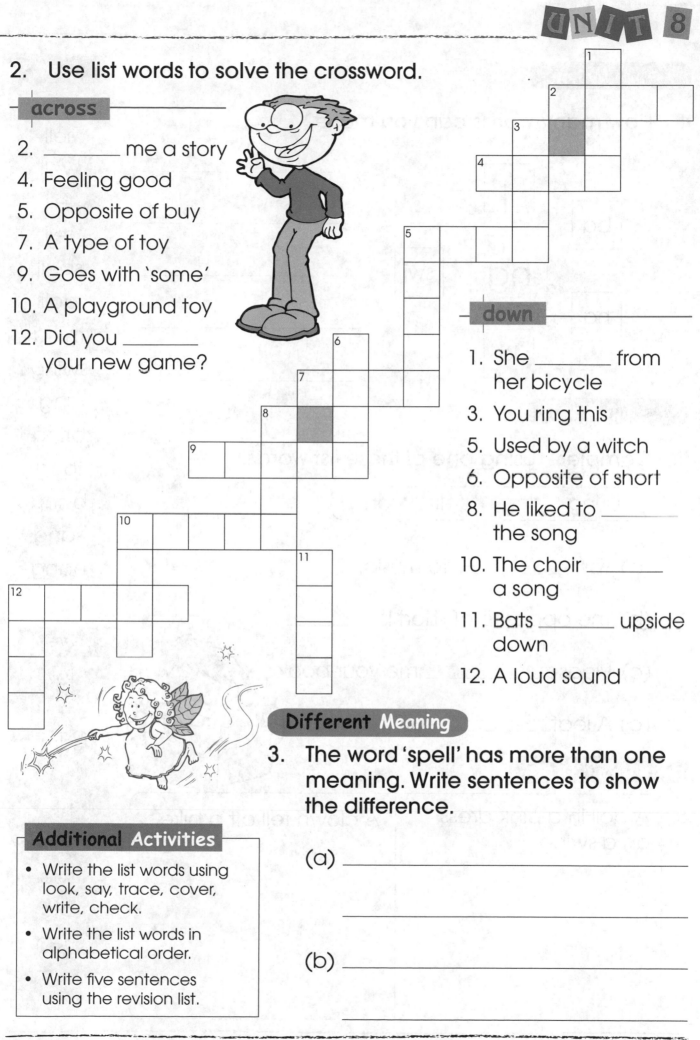

across

2. _____ me a story
4. Feeling good
5. Opposite of buy
7. A type of toy
9. Goes with 'some'
10. A playground toy
12. Did you _____ your new game?

down

1. She _____ from her bicycle
3. You ring this
5. Used by a witch
6. Opposite of short
8. He liked to _____ the song
10. The choir _____ a song
11. Bats _____ upside down
12. A loud sound

Different Meaning

3. The word 'spell' has more than one meaning. Write sentences to show the difference.

(a) _____

_____

(b) _____

_____

Additional Activities

• Write the list words using look, say, trace, cover, write, check.
• Write the list words in alphabetical order.
• Write five sentences using the revision list.

Word Maker

4. How many words can you make?

si

ba

ng   swi

ha

lo

_____

_____

_____

_____

_____

List

bell
sell
well
fell
tell
spell
doll
thing
swing
sing
bring
long
bang
sang
hang

Missing Words

5. Complete, using one of these list words.

> bring   sing   fell   long

(a) You _____ to music.

(b) The opposite of short is _____.

(c) Please _____ me your book.

(d) A leaf _____ off the tree.

Read and Draw

6.

A doll in a pink dress on a swing.	A clown fell off a bike.

Revision

jog
rut
him
we
hid
come
see
big
beg
hum

7. **Find these list words in the word search.**

bell	swing	sell
sing	well	bring
fell	long	tell
bang	spell	sang
doll	hang	thing

s	w	i	n	g	x	c	k	s
w	e	l	l	s	t	l	j	e
s	s	i	n	g	d	o	l	l
p	b	a	n	g	y	n	z	l
e	h	a	n	g	s	g	b	t
l	r	j	f	y	a	t	r	h
l	q	w	e	x	n	e	i	i
t	b	e	l	l	g	l	n	n
i	n	w	l	p	d	l	g	g

Memory Master

8. (a) Cover the list words. Write two from memory.

   _____ _____

   (b) Write a sentence using both words.

   _____

   _____

Synonyms

9. Write the list word with a similiar meaning.

   (a) hit _____

   (b) say _____

   (c) dropped _____

Word Hunt

10.

bring	doll	fell	swing
long	bang	spell	tell

   (a) Which list word could be found at a park?

   _____

   (b) Put a black circle around the 'ng' words.

   (c) Which words rhyme with sell?

   _____ _____ _____

List Words	Test 1	Test 2	Test 3	Test 4	Test 5	T
chop						
chin						
much						
rich						
such						
punch						
lunch						
chick						
miss						
dress						
mess						
loss						
toss						
cross						
you						

Look Say Trace Cover Write Check

Difficult Words I Have Found	Test 1	Test 2	Test 3	T

Picture Matching

1. Write the list word that matches each picture.

(a)

(b)

(c)

(d)

2. Use list words to solve the crossword.

across

2. Opposite of a tick
4. He felt bad about the _____ of the game
6. A baby chicken
7. It was _____ a nice day that we went for a walk in the park
9. Part of your face
10. Opposite to poor
12. Girls may wear one

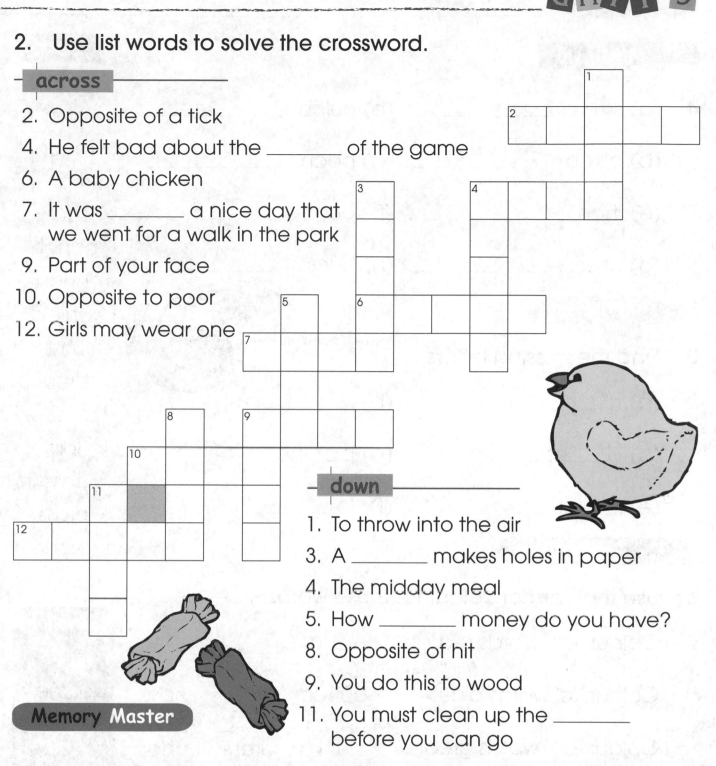

down

1. To throw into the air
3. A _____ makes holes in paper
4. The midday meal
5. How _____ money do you have?
8. Opposite of hit
9. You do this to wood
11. You must clean up the _____ before you can go

Memory Master

3. Circle the correctly spelled word from the three choices below. Write each from memory.

(a) | cop | chop | chopp | _____

(b) | punch | punnch | puntch | _____

(c) | chik | chick | chikk | _____

UNIT 9

All Mixed Up

4. (a) smis _____   (b) nulch _____

    (b) cikch _____   (d) poch _____

    (e) ihcn _____   (f) ouy _____

    (g) scors _____   (h) hucs _____

Missing Letters

5. Find the missing letters.

    (a) r___c___   (b) ___ ___op

    (c) d___es___   (d) p___nc___

    (e) ___ros___   (f) lo___ ___

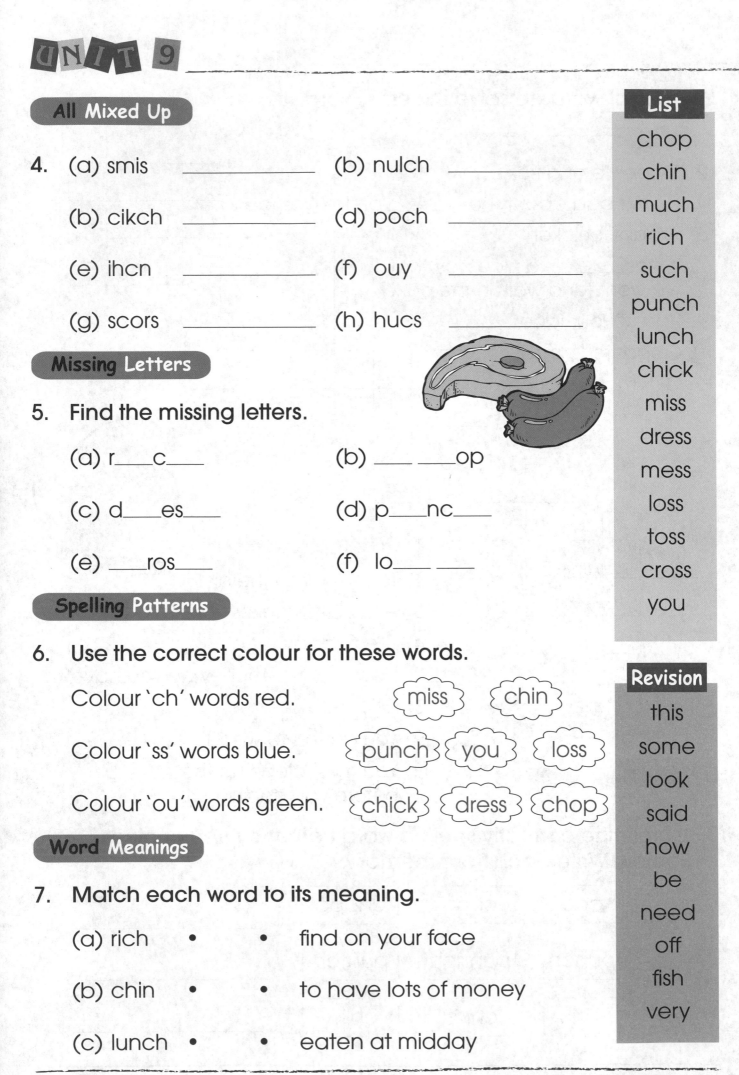

Spelling Patterns

6. Use the correct colour for these words.

    Colour 'ch' words red.   miss   chin

    Colour 'ss' words blue.   punch   you   loss

    Colour 'ou' words green.   chick   dress   chop

Word Meanings

7. Match each word to its meaning.

    (a) rich •   • find on your face

    (b) chin •   • to have lots of money

    (c) lunch •   • eaten at midday

List

chop
chin
much
rich
such
punch
lunch
chick
miss
dress
mess
loss
toss
cross
you

Revision

this
some
look
said
how
be
need
off
fish
very

8. **Find these list words in the word search.**

chop   chick
chin   miss
much   dress
rich   mess
such   loss
punch   toss
lunch   cross

s	r	p	u	n	c	h	m	p
t	i	d	t	o	s	s	z	c
c	c	r	l	e	m	u	c	h
h	h	e	l	y	i	y	m	i
o	c	s	l	o	s	k	e	n
p	r	s	s	u	s	j	s	s
g	o	l	u	n	c	h	s	x
r	s	d	c	l	o	s	s	e
e	s	c	h	i	c	k	x	d

Word Maker

9. **How many words can you make?**

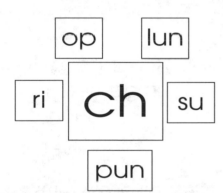

_____

_____

_____

_____

_____

Word Worm

10. Circle each list word you can find in the word worm.

richdresschicklossyousuchchop

Fill in the Gap

11. **Fill in the gap.**

(a) lunch

lunc____

lun____ ____

lu____ ____ ____

l____ ____ ____ ____

_____

(b) cross

cros____

cro____ ____

cr____ ____ ____

c____ ____ ____ ____

_____

(c) punch

punc____

pun____ ____

pu____ ____ ____

p____ ____ ____ ____

_____

List Words	Test 1	Test 2	Test 3	Test 4	Test 5	T
three						
thin						
thick						
moth						
cloth						
with						
cake						
wake						
take						
gate						
ate						
name						
came						
gave						
game						

Look   Say   Trace   Cover   Write   Check

Difficult Words I Have Found	Test 1	Test 2	Test 3	T

Secret Words

1. (a) Take 'th' off thin.

_____

(b) Rhymes with cake but starts with 'b'.

_____

(c) Change 'th' to 'f' in thin.

_____

(d) Change 'g' to 's' in game.

_____

(e) Rhymes with ate but starts with 'l'.

_____

(f) Take 'e' off ate.

_____

2. Use list words to solve the crossword.

across

2. You can walk through it
4. Can you _____ him up?
5. Clothes are made from _____
8. Opposite of thick
10. A type of flying insect
11. She _____ to our place
13. Eaten at birthday parties

down

1. I _____ the cake yesterday
3. Four _____ away one is three
4. Come _____ me
6. Opposite of thin
7. A person is called by his or her _____
8. One, two, _____
9. Who _____ me this present?
12. Cricket is a _____

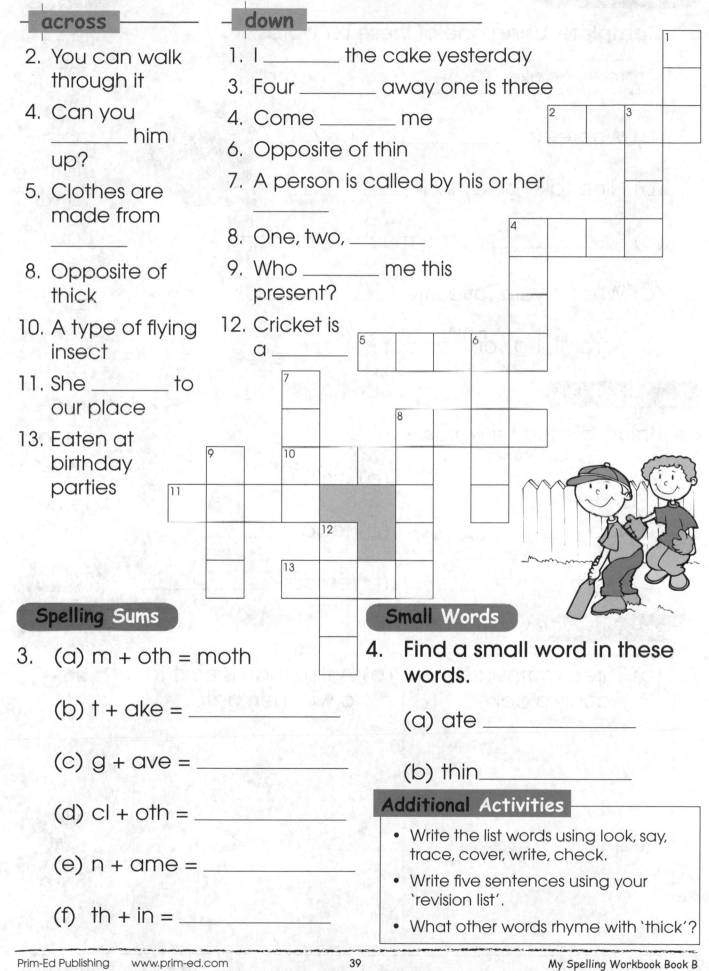

Spelling Sums

3. (a) m + oth = moth

   (b) t + ake = _____

   (c) g + ave = _____

   (d) cl + oth = _____

   (e) n + ame = _____

   (f) th + in = _____

Small Words

4. Find a small word in these words.

   (a) ate _____

   (b) thin _____

Additional Activities

- Write the list words using look, say, trace, cover, write, check.
- Write five sentences using your 'revision list'.
- What other words rhyme with 'thick'?

UNIT 10

List

three
thin
thick
moth
cloth
with
cake
wake
take
gate
ate
name
came
gave
game

Missing Words

5. Complete, using one of these list words.

three   cake   ate   you   game

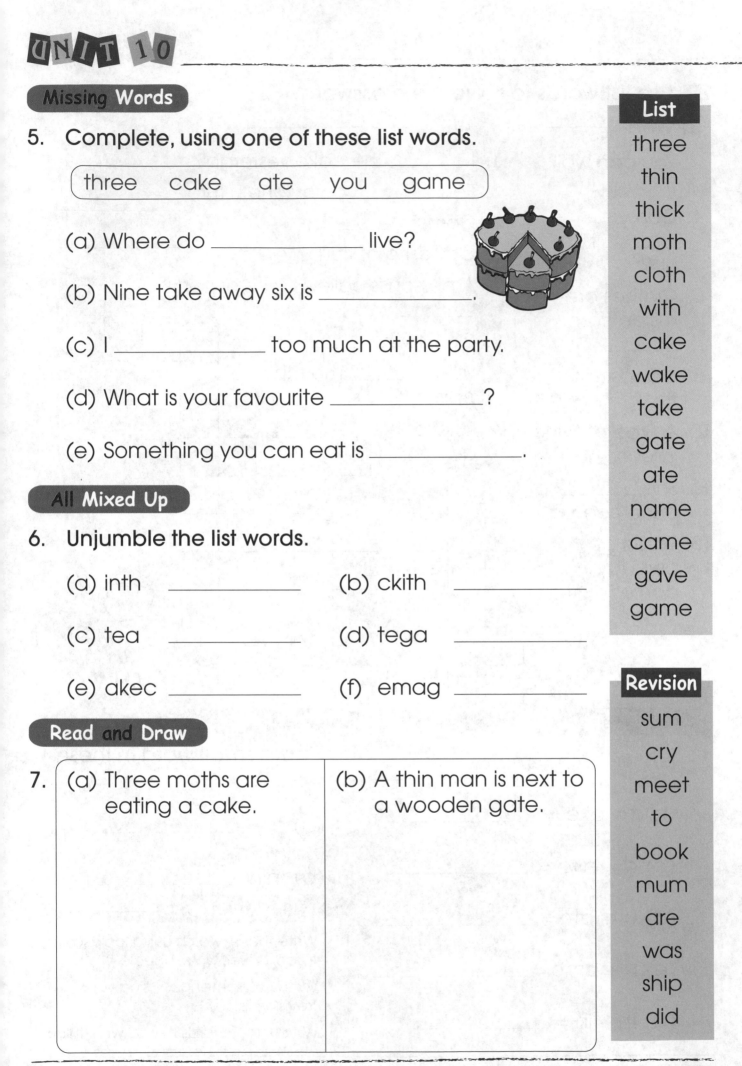

(a) Where do _____ live?

(b) Nine take away six is _____.

(c) I _____ too much at the party.

(d) What is your favourite _____?

(e) Something you can eat is _____.

All Mixed Up

6. Unjumble the list words.

(a) inth _____   (b) ckith _____

(c) tea _____   (d) tega _____

(e) akec _____   (f) emag _____

Read and Draw

7.

(a) Three moths are eating a cake.	(b) A thin man is next to a wooden gate.

Revision

sum
cry
meet
to
book
mum
are
was
ship
did

8. **Find these list words in the word search.**

three   take

thin   gate

thick   ate

moth   name

cloth   came

with   gave

cake   game

wake

j	b	c	w	i	t	h	k	c
a	n	t	c	g	a	t	e	l
t	a	h	a	x	k	j	c	o
e	m	r	k	c	e	k	a	t
m	e	e	e	y	s	l	m	h
t	g	e	m	g	a	v	e	v
h	a	p	o	o	z	b	y	q
i	m	z	t	w	a	k	e	u
n	e	t	h	i	c	k	u	r

Additional Activities

9. **Put these words into alphabetical order.**

came   moth   thick   ate   game

_____

What am I?

10. (a) I am an insect that can fly.

I rhyme with cloth.

I am a _____.

(b) I am found at birthday parties.

You can eat me.

I am a _____.

(c) I am a number.

I come before four.

I am _____.

(d) I can be open and shut.

I rhyme with ate.

I am a _____.

UNIT 11

List Words	Test 1	Test 2	Test 3	Test 4	Test 5	T
fern						
her						
under						
ever						
saw						
never						
make						
live						
spoon						
tooth						
zoo						
roof						
cool						
snack						
back						

Look   Say   Trace   Cover   Write   Check

Difficult Words I Have Found	Test 1	Test 2	Test 3	T

1. Look at each picture. Circle the correct word. Write it on the line.

(a)

spoon/spoons

_____

(b)

fern/ferns

_____

(c)

snack/snacks

_____

What am I?

2. I am hard.
I can fall out.
I live in your mouth.

I am a _____.

3. Use list words to solve the crossword.

across

2. Found in your mouth

4. A type of plant

6. Opposite of over

9. Today I see, yesterday I _____

10. Food eaten between meals

12. Yesterday I 'made', today I _____

13. The top of a house

14. Opposite of dead

down

1. A place where animals can be seen

3. Opposite of him

5. They lived happily _____ after

7. Opposite of always

8. Opposite of front

9. You eat with it

11. Opposite of warm

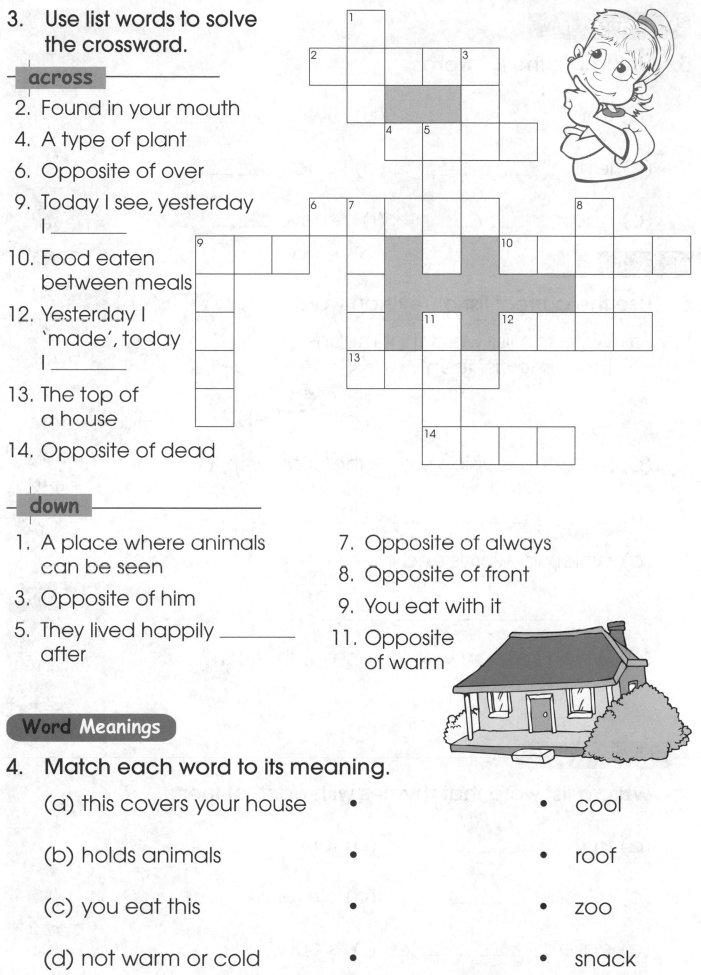

Word Meanings

4. Match each word to its meaning.

(a) this covers your house   •   • cool

(b) holds animals   •   • roof

(c) you eat this   •   • zoo

(d) not warm or cold   •   • snack

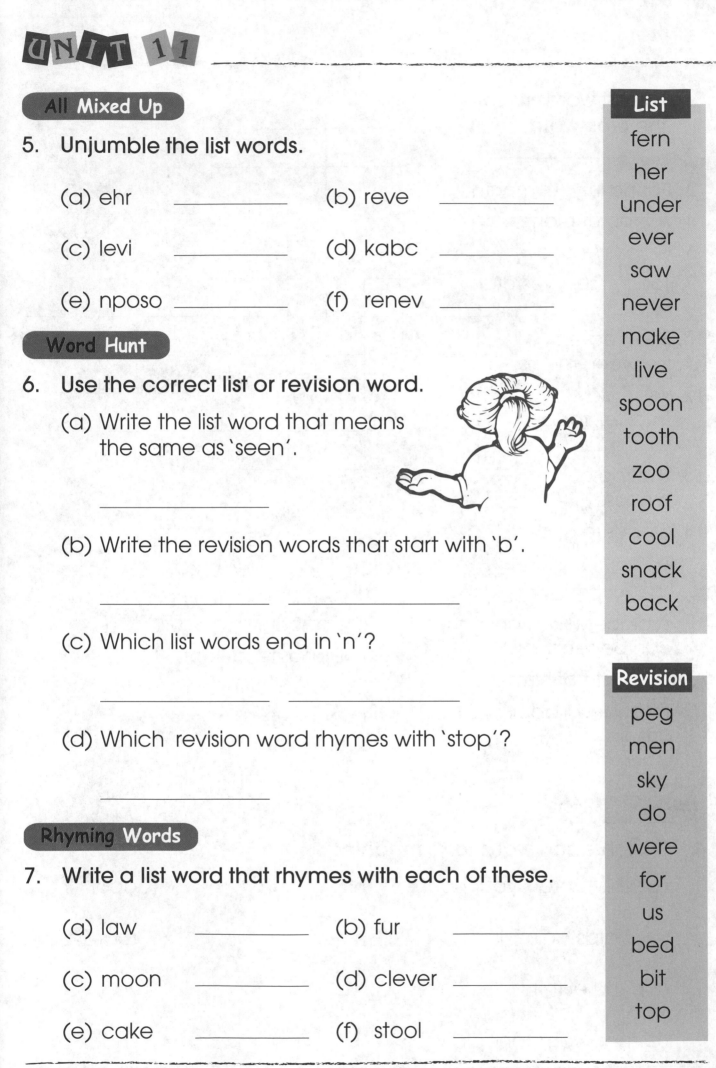

UNIT 11 _____

All Mixed Up

5. Unjumble the list words.

(a) ehr _____   (b) reve _____

(c) levi _____   (d) kabc _____

(e) nposo _____   (f) renev _____

Word Hunt

6. Use the correct list or revision word.

(a) Write the list word that means the same as 'seen'.

_____

(b) Write the revision words that start with 'b'.

_____   _____

(c) Which list words end in 'n'?

_____   _____

(d) Which revision word rhymes with 'stop'?

_____

Rhyming Words

7. Write a list word that rhymes with each of these.

(a) law _____   (b) fur _____

(c) moon _____   (d) clever _____

(e) cake _____   (f) stool _____

List

fern
her
under
ever
saw
never
make
live
spoon
tooth
zoo
roof
cool
snack
back

Revision

peg
men
sky
do
were
for
us
bed
bit
top

8. **Find these list words in the word search.**

b	a	c	k	h	e	r	x	s
q	u	s	t	n	l	s	z	p
u	n	d	e	r	i	n	o	o
r	e	y	v	p	v	a	o	o
o	n	o	e	q	e	c	y	n
o	d	u	r	z	r	k	t	m
f	e	r	n	c	o	o	l	a
t	o	o	t	h	p	t	k	k
n	e	v	e	r	s	a	w	e

fern   spoon

her   tooth

under   ever

roof   saw

back   never

snack   make

cool   live

zoo

Memory Master

9. (a) Cover the list words. Write two from memory.

   _____   _____

   (b) Write a sentence using both words.

   _____

   _____

Compound Words

10. **Join to make compound words.**

    (a) tooth •   • ground

    (b) bed   •   • bone

    (c) under •   • room

    (d) her   •   • brush

    (e) back   •   • self

Synonyms

11. **Find a list word with a similar meaning.**

    (a) chilly _____

    (b) below   _____

    (c) meal   _____

List Words	Test 1	Test 2	Test 3	Test 4	Test 5	T
car						
star						
arm						
farm						
hard						
far						
start						
bone						
tone						
home						
rope						
hope						
note						
cone						
just						

Look   Say   Trace   Cover   Write   Check

Difficult Words I Have Found	Test 1	Test 2	Test 3	T

Word Worm

1. Circle each list word you can find in the word worm.

ropestartonefarmjustbonenote

What am I?

2. I come out at night.

I twinkle.

You see me in the sky.

I am a _____.

Additional Activities

- Write the list words using look, say, trace, cover, write, check.
- Write the list words in alphabetical order.
- List five more words that start with 'st'.

3. **Use list words to solve the crossword.**

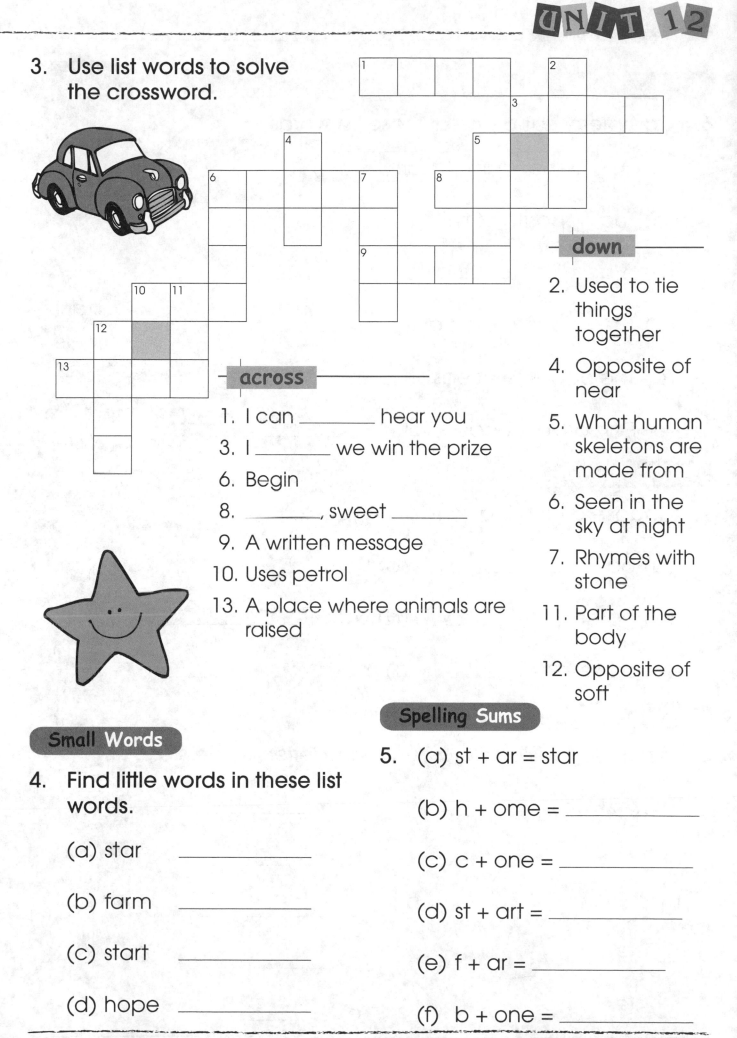

across

1. I can _____ hear you
3. I _____ we win the prize
6. Begin
8. _____, sweet _____
9. A written message
10. Uses petrol
13. A place where animals are raised

down

2. Used to tie things together
4. Opposite of near
5. What human skeletons are made from
6. Seen in the sky at night
7. Rhymes with stone
11. Part of the body
12. Opposite of soft

Small Words

4. **Find little words in these list words.**

(a) star _____

(b) farm _____

(c) start _____

(d) hope _____

Spelling Sums

5. (a) st + ar = star

(b) h + ome = _____

(c) c + one = _____

(d) st + art = _____

(e) f + ar = _____

(f) b + one = _____

Missing Words

6. Complete, using one of these list words

> start   bone   arm   hard   far

(a) The opposite of finish is _____.

(b) A dog likes to eat a _____.

(c) The opposite of near is _____.

(d) The opposite of easy is _____.

(e) Part of your body is your _____.

Rhyming Words

7. Choose a rhyming word from your list.

(a) bar _____   (b) harm _____

(c) card _____   (d) vote _____

(e) stone _____   (f) part _____

Letters into Words

8. Write five revision words, using the letters in the stars.

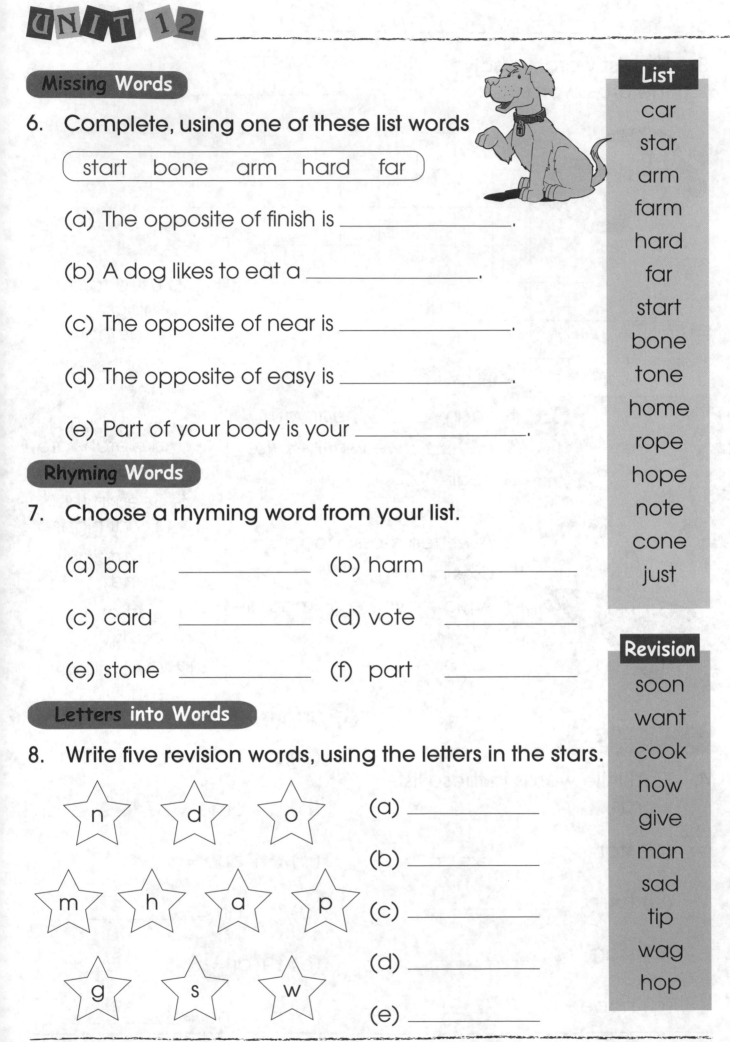

(a) _____

(b) _____

(c) _____

(d) _____

(e) _____

List

car
star
arm
farm
hard
far
start
bone
tone
home
rope
hope
note
cone
just

Revision

soon
want
cook
now
give
man
sad
tip
wag
hop

9. **Find these list words in the word search.**

car	bone
star	tone
arm	home
farm	rope
hard	hope
far	just
start	cone
note	

p	s	h	t	h	n	c	a	r
s	t	a	r	w	n	r	z	f
q	a	r	t	b	o	o	u	a
f	r	d	h	o	t	p	z	r
a	t	z	e	n	e	e	q	m
r	t	h	y	e	c	o	n	e
a	t	o	n	e	h	o	p	e
e	y	m	y	j	u	s	t	j
s	i	e	x	m	a	r	m	i

Shape Sorter

10. **Guess the word by its shape.**

(a)

(b)

(c)

(d)

(e)

(f)

Secret Words

11. (a) Add 's' to tone. _____

(b) Change 'o' to 'i' in rope. _____

(c) Take off 'h' in home and add 's'. _____

(d) Change 'd' to 'p' in hard. _____

UNIT 13

List Words	Test 1	Test 2	Test 3	Test 4	Test 5	T
leaf						
sea						
tea						
meat						
seat						
clean						
eat						
read						
mean						
boy						
toy						
joy						
than						
that						
them						

Look   Say   Trace   Cover   Write   Check

Difficult Words I Have Found	Test 1	Test 2	Test 3	T

Picture Matching

1. Write the list word that matches each picture

(a)

_____

(b)

_____

(c)

_____

(d)

_____

2. Use list words to solve the crossword.

Word Hunt

3. (a) Which list word is kept in the fridge?

_____

(b) Which list words rhyme with pea?

_____

_____

(c) Which list word can you swim in?

_____

(d) Which list word can you drink?

_____

across

1. Something you sit on
4. To take in food
5. Part of a tree
6. I heard _____ talk
7. A type of food
8. May I have more _____ that please?
9. Can you _____ that book?
11. Opposite of girl

down

1. Similar to ocean
2. A drink
3. Opposite of dirty
6. Is _____ your toy?
7. Nasty
8. Something you play with
10. Happiness

All Mixed Up

4. Unjumble the list words.

(a) dear _____   (b) eat _____

(c) yob _____   (d) atth _____

(e) emth _____   (f) yot _____

(g) flea _____   (h) neam _____

List

leaf
sea
tea
meat
seat
clean
eat
read
mean
boy
toy
joy
than
that
them

Missing Words

5. Complete, using one of these list words.

boy   that   mean   clean   leaf   eat

(a) This grows on a tree. _____

(b) The opposite of girl is _____.

(c) _____ is my house.

(d) The opposite of dirty is _____.

(e) The opposite of kind is _____.

(f) I like to _____ ice-cream.

Spelling Patterns

6. Use the correct colour for these words.

(a) Colour the 'th' words red.   them   boy   that

(b) Colour the 'oy' words blue.   toy   sea   seat

(c) Colour the 'ea' words green.   joy   mean   boy

Revision

pan
had
mat
net
tap
fed
run
by
room
when

7. **Find these list words in the word search.**

leaf   sea

boy   tea

toy   meat

joy   seat

than   clean

that   eat

them   read

mean

b	n	j	s	j	o	y	g	e
o	s	t	e	h	t	h	e	m
y	e	o	a	j	z	x	t	e
l	a	y	t	h	a	t	h	a
e	z	x	e	a	t	w	a	t
a	p	r	t	a	i	s	n	h
f	m	c	l	e	a	n	g	i
n	r	e	a	d	b	b	m	t
k	m	m	e	a	n	t	e	a

Alphabetical Order

8. **Write these list words in alphabetical order.**

tea   boy   eat   sea   clean

_____

Secret Words

9.   (a) Add 'm' to tea.   _____

    (b) Take 'th' off that.   _____

    (c) Rhymes with mean, but starts with 'b'. _____

    (d) Take 't' off meat and put in 'l'.   _____

    (e) Take 'a' off sea and put in 'e'.   _____

    (f) Rhymes with than, but starts with 'f'.   _____

    (g) Take 'ea' off seat and put in 'i'.   _____

    (h) Take 'a' off from meat and put in 'e'. _____

List Words	Test 1	Test 2	Test 3	Test 4	Test 5	T
all						
ball						
call						
fall						
hall						
wall						
tall						
small						
sky						
dry						
try						
fly						
each						
teach						
beach						

Look   Say   Trace   Cover   Write   Check

Difficult Words I Have Found	Test 1	Test 2	Test 3	T

Letters into Words

1. Write four list words using the letters in the wall.

	y	
a	s	l
	w	h
l	k	m

_____

_____

_____

_____

What am I?

2. I have no corners.
   I am light.
   You throw and
   catch me.

   I am a _____.

3. **Use list words to solve the crossword.**

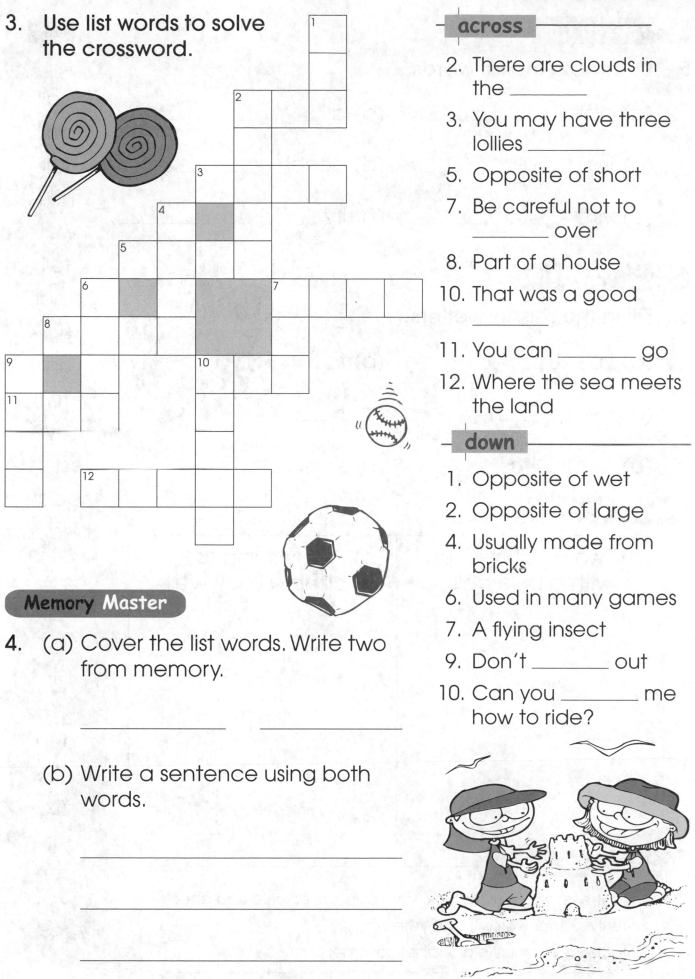

across

2. There are clouds in the _____
3. You may have three lollies _____
5. Opposite of short
7. Be careful not to _____ over
8. Part of a house
10. That was a good _____
11. You can _____ go
12. Where the sea meets the land

down

1. Opposite of wet
2. Opposite of large
4. Usually made from bricks
6. Used in many games
7. A flying insect
9. Don't _____ out
10. Can you _____ me how to ride?

Memory Master

4. (a) Cover the list words. Write two from memory.

_____   _____

(b) Write a sentence using both words.

_____

_____

_____

All Mixed Up

5. Unjumble the list words.

(a) abll _____

(b) afll _____

(c) ltal _____

(d) acebh _____

(e) ysk _____

(f) lfy _____

Missing Letters

6. Fill in the missing letters.

(a) b___l___

(b) f___y

(c) be___ ___h

(d) tr___

(e) t___ ___c___

(f) ___k___

Read and Draw

7.

(a) Two small children with a blue ball.	(b) A boy trying to climb a brick wall.

List

all
ball
call
fall
hall
wall
tall
small
sky
dry
try
fly
each
teach
beach

Revision

log
pin
rip
pup
pet
fix
fun
pen
bee
wish

Additional Activities

• Write the list words using look, say, trace, cover, write and check.

• Write five other words that rhyme with sky.

• Write the revision list in alphabetical order

8. **Find these list words in the word search.**

all	try
ball	fly
call	fall
hall	wall
each	tall
teach	small
beach	shy
dry	

b	n	j	s	j	m	y	z	e
b	a	l	l	w	y	m	j	a
x	b	u	h	a	l	l	q	c
c	e	d	s	l	f	t	r	h
a	a	r	h	l	l	a	c	s
l	c	y	y	b	y	l	y	m
l	h	v	g	a	l	l	u	a
t	e	a	c	h	r	y	b	l
w	f	a	l	l	t	r	y	l

Word Meanings

9. **Match each word to its meaning.**

(a) fly   •   • opposite of wet

(b) small   •   • to drop

(c) dry   •   • a place to swim

(d) fall   •   • an insect

(e) beach   •   • little

Word Hunt

10. | teach   sky   cry   ball   fall   tall   beach   wall |

(a) Which words rhyme with 'all'?

_____ _____ _____ _____

(b) Write the longest words. _____ _____

(c) List the words with 'y' in them. _____ _____

List Words	Test 1	Test 2	Test 3	Test 4	Test 5	T
coat						
boat						
float						
wink						
toast						
load						
road						
loaf						
soak						
goat						
ink						
sink						
drink						
think						
pink						

Look   Say   Trace   Cover   Write   Check

Difficult Words I Have Found	Test 1	Test 2	Test 3	T

Picture Matching

1. Circle the correct word.

(a)

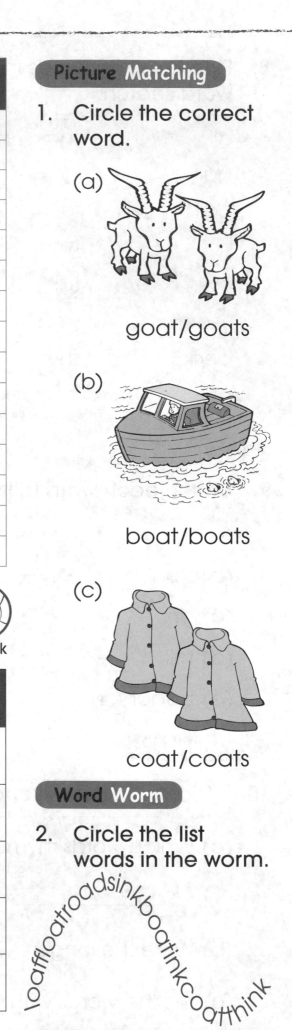

goat/goats

(b)

boat/boats

(c)

coat/coats

Word Worm

2. Circle the list words in the worm.

loaffloatroadsinkboatinkcoatthink

3. Use list words to solve the crossword.

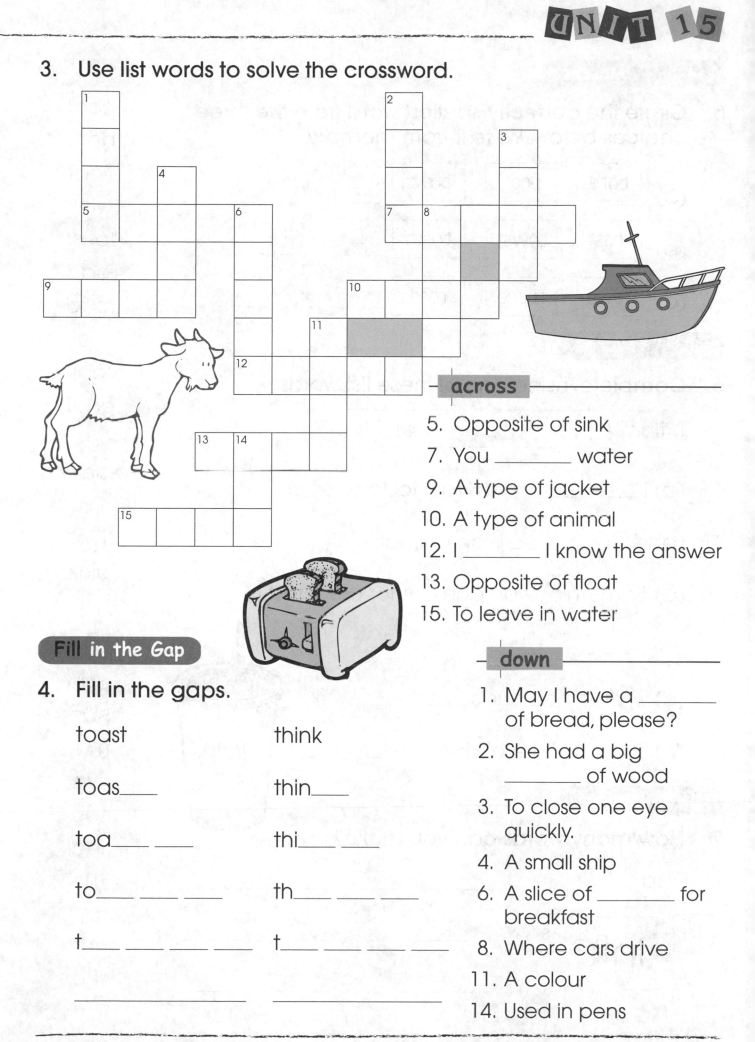

across

5. Opposite of sink
7. You _____ water
9. A type of jacket
10. A type of animal
12. I _____ I know the answer
13. Opposite of float
15. To leave in water

down

1. May I have a _____ of bread, please?
2. She had a big _____ of wood
3. To close one eye quickly.
4. A small ship
6. A slice of _____ for breakfast
8. Where cars drive
11. A colour
14. Used in pens

Fill in the Gap

4. Fill in the gaps.

toast   think

toas___   thin___

toa___ ___   thi___ ___

to___ ___ ___ th___ ___ ___

t___ ___ ___ ___   t___ ___ ___ ___

_____   _____

Memory Master

5. Circle the correctly spelled word from the three choices below. Write it from memory.

(a) | bote | boat | bowt | _____

(b) | toast | towst | toste | _____

(c) | rowd | roade | road | _____

Missing Words

6. Complete, using one of these list words

think   pink   goat   toast   float

(a) I _____ it will rain today.

(b) A _____ is an animal.

(c) Something you can eat for breakfast is

_____.

(d) A pretty colour is _____.

(e) The opposite of sink is _____.

Word Maker

7. How many words can you make?

p   dr   _____   _____

th   ink   s   _____   _____

l   w   _____   _____

List

coat
boat
float
wink
toast
load
road
loaf
soak
goat
ink
sink
drink
think
pink

Revision

pan
had
mat
net
tap
fed
run
by
room
when

8. **Find these list words in the word search.**

coat   soak

boat   goat

float   ink

sink   toast

drink   load

think   road

pink   loaf

wink

y	a	u	r	d	r	i	n	k
i	n	k	w	i	n	k	t	w
l	o	a	d	a	i	l	b	r
p	i	n	k	t	s	o	o	g
c	s	i	n	k	x	a	a	t
o	t	h	i	n	k	f	t	o
a	i	n	q	s	o	a	k	a
t	r	o	a	d	z	p	y	s
g	o	a	t	f	l	o	a	t

Mixed up Sentences

9. **Unjumble the sentences.**

(a) coat   is   pink.   My

_____

(b) your   Put   sink.   on   the   drink

_____

(c) can   I   sea.   float   the   on

_____

What am I?

10. I am made of metal.

I have a drain.

You wash your plates in me.

I am a

_____.

Word Hunt

11. **The answers to these riddles have 'oa' in them.**

(a) I am made from bread and you eat me at breakfast.

I am _____.

(b) Be careful crossing me. Cars drive on me.

I am a _____.

UNIT 16

List Words	Test 1	Test 2	Test 3	Test 4	Test 5	T
tray						
say						
may						
stay						
way						
play						
hay						
lay						
pay						
girl						
first						
third						
bird						
shirt						
dirt						

Look   Say   Trace   Cover   Write   Check

Difficult Words I Have Found	Test 1	Test 2	Test 3	T

Spelling Sums

1. (a) m + ay = may

    (b) pl + ay = _____

    (c) tr + ay = _____

    (d) h + ay = _____

    (e) b + ird = _____

    (f) d + irt = _____

What am I?

2. I have wings.
    I love to eat seeds.
    I am many colours.

    I am a _____.

Correct Words

3. Circle the correct word.

    (a) Six (girl/girls) came to my party.

    (b) Stack all the (tray/trays) on the bench.

    (c) Tom's (shirt/shirts) had a dirty mark.

4. **Use list words to solve the crossword.**

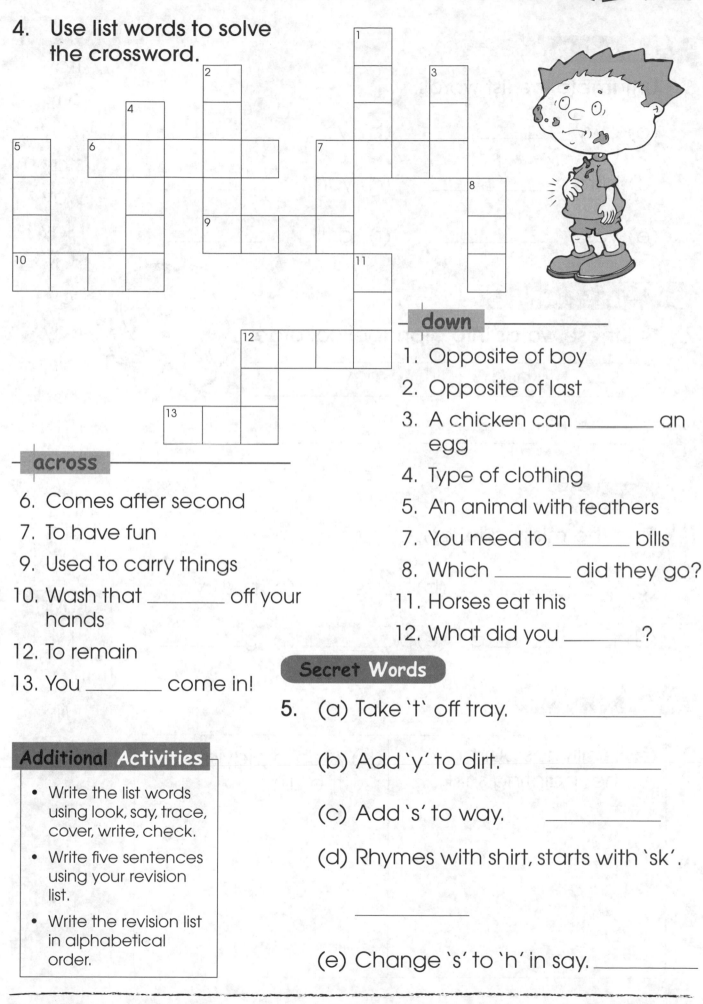

across

6. Comes after second
7. To have fun
9. Used to carry things
10. Wash that _____ off your hands
12. To remain
13. You _____ come in!

down

1. Opposite of boy
2. Opposite of last
3. A chicken can _____ an egg
4. Type of clothing
5. An animal with feathers
7. You need to _____ bills
8. Which _____ did they go?
11. Horses eat this
12. What did you _____?

Secret Words

5. (a) Take 't' off tray. _____

(b) Add 'y' to dirt. _____

(c) Add 's' to way. _____

(d) Rhymes with shirt, starts with 'sk'.

_____

(e) Change 's' to 'h' in say. _____

Additional Activities

- Write the list words using look, say, trace, cover, write, check.
- Write five sentences using your revision list.
- Write the revision list in alphabetical order.

All Mixed Up

6. Unjumble the list words.

   (a) awy _____   (b) lya _____

   (c) hitrd _____   (d) yart _____

   (e) yas _____   (f) drit _____

Alphabetical Order

7. Put these words into alphabetical order.

   | say | bird | girl | may | way |

   _____

Missing Letters

8. Find the missing letters.

   (a) s___ ___ ___   (b) ___ ___rt (c) p___y

   (d) t___ ___ ___d (e) w___ ___ (f) gi___ ___

Read and Draw

9.
(a) A girl has put on her painting shirt.	(b) A child playing in the dirt.

List

tray
say
may
stay
way
play
hay
lay
pay
girl
first
third
bird
shirt
dirt

Revision

lot
mad
hip
fat
pit
cap
nut
bun
ten
sip

10. **Find these list words in the word search.**

tray	pay
say	girl
may	first
stay	third
way	bird
play	dirt
hay	shirt
lay	

x	z	w	h	t	t	j	d	h
i	n	a	b	i	r	d	i	a
s	a	y	u	g	a	m	r	y
g	p	l	a	y	y	o	t	s
i	p	a	u	t	w	m	a	y
r	a	t	h	i	r	d	s	q
l	y	t	h	s	l	a	y	z
s	f	i	r	s	t	p	m	j
s	t	a	y	s	h	i	r	t

Word Meanings

11. **Match each word to its meaning.**

(a) shirt •   • something to wear

(b) dirt •   • used to carry things

(c) tray •   • comes after second

(d) third •   • found on the ground

Word Maker

12. **How many words can you make?**

pl   tr

w   p

ay

st   s

h   l

_____   _____

_____   _____

_____   _____

_____   _____

UNIT 17

List Words	Test 1	Test 2	Test 3	Test 4	Test 5	T
fork						
born						
for						
forgot						
torn						
short						
whip						
which						
hold						
gold						
sold						
told						
fold						
cold						
old						

Look   Say   Trace   Cover   Write   Check

Difficult Words I Have Found	Test 1	Test 2	Test 3	T

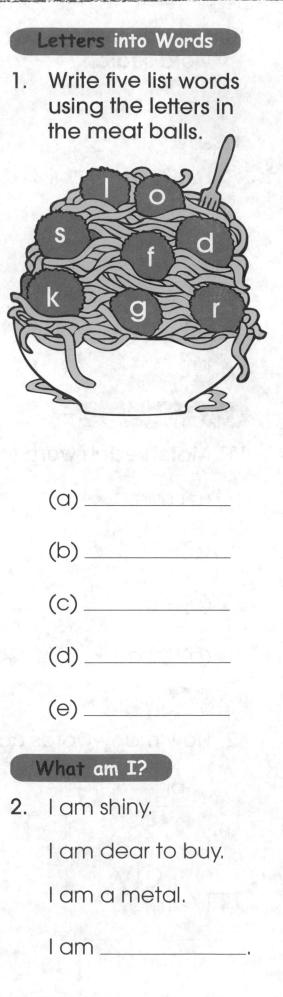

Letters into Words

1. Write five list words using the letters in the meat balls.

(a) _____

(b) _____

(c) _____

(d) _____

(e) _____

What am I?

2. I am shiny.

I am dear to buy.

I am a metal.

I am _____.

3. Use list words to solve the crossword.

across

2. Opposite of young

5. Opposite of hot

6. Knife and _____

8. The teacher _____ us a story

9. This is _____ you

10. _____ on tight!

13. The page was _____ out of the book

14. _____ way did they go?

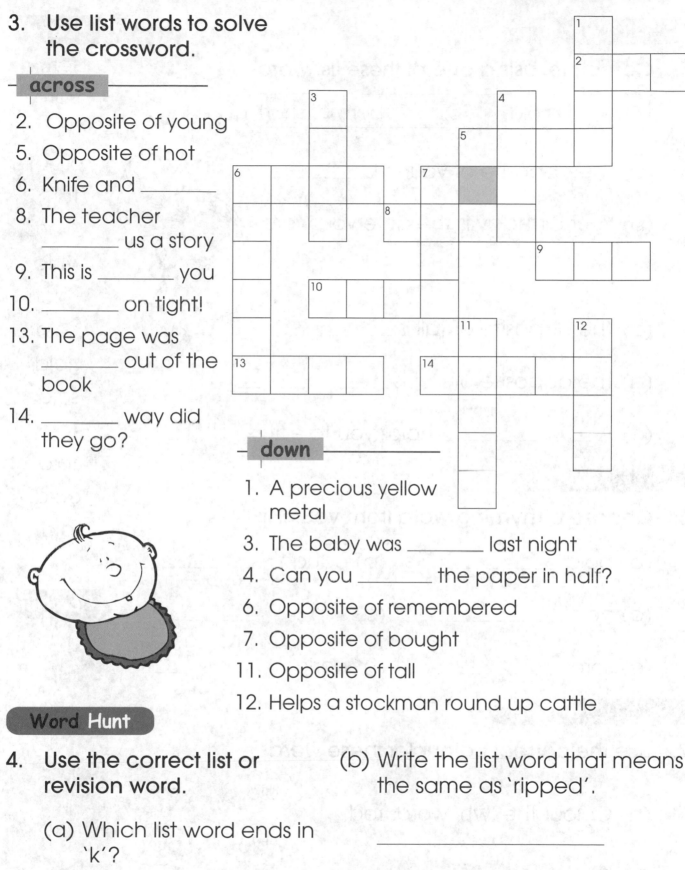

down

1. A precious yellow metal

3. The baby was _____ last night

4. Can you _____ the paper in half?

6. Opposite of remembered

7. Opposite of bought

11. Opposite of tall

12. Helps a stockman round up cattle

Word Hunt

4. Use the correct list or revision word.

(a) Which list word ends in 'k'?

_____

(b) Write the list word that means the same as 'ripped'.

_____

(c) Which revision word rhymes with peg?

_____

UNIT 17

List

Missing Words

5. Complete, using one of these list words.

    | fork | cold | old | born | short |

    (a) The opposite of young is _____

    (b) Your birthday is the date you were

    _____.

    (c) The opposite of tall is _____.

    (d) The opposite of hot is _____.

    (e) A _____ helps you to eat.

Rhyming Words

6. Choose a rhyming word from your list.

    (a) bold _____   (b) caught _____

    (c) horn _____   (d) skip _____

    (e) sore _____   (f) cork _____

Spelling Patterns

7. Use the correct colour for these words.

    (a) Colour the 'wh' words red.

    (b) Colour the 'or' words blue.

    (c) Colour the 'old' words green.

    old   sold
    whip   born
    which torn
    forgot gold

List

fork
born
for
forgot
torn
short
whip
which
hold
gold
sold
told
fold
cold
old

Revision

rat
up
tag
rap
box
leg
or
hug
she
rid

8. **Find these list words in the word search.**

fork	which
born	hold
gold	forgot
sold	torn
told	short
fold	cold
old	whip

h	w	f	o	r	y	b	j	u
o	z	f	o	r	g	o	t	f
l	c	o	l	d	i	r	w	r
d	t	s	o	l	d	n	h	r
j	o	q	n	o	n	g	i	t
x	r	g	o	l	d	q	p	o
a	n	w	h	i	c	h	o	l
f	o	r	k	g	f	o	l	d
o	s	h	o	r	t	o	d	w

Memory Master

9. Cover the list words. Write two from memory.

_____   _____

Write a sentence using both words.

_____

_____

Shape Sorter

10. **Guess the word by its shape.**

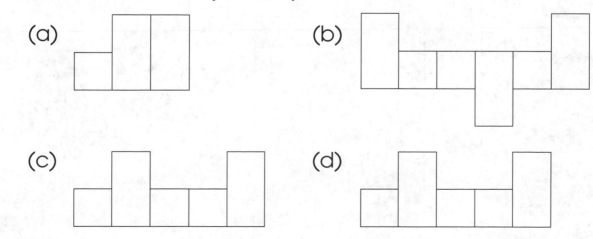

(a)

(b)

(c)

(d)

List Words	Test 1	Test 2	Test 3	Test 4	Test 5	T
owl						
frown						
down						
town						
brown						
clown						
rain						
train						
tail						
bait						
wait						
sail						
nail						
snail						
main						

Look   Say   Trace   Cover   Write   Check

Difficult Words I Have Found	Test 1	Test 2	Test 3	T

Picture Matching

1. Look at each picture. Circle the correct word. Write it on the line.

(a)

(snail/snails)

_____

(b)

(sail/sails)

_____

(c)

(train/trains)

_____

(d)

(owl/owls)

_____

2. Use list words to solve the crossword.

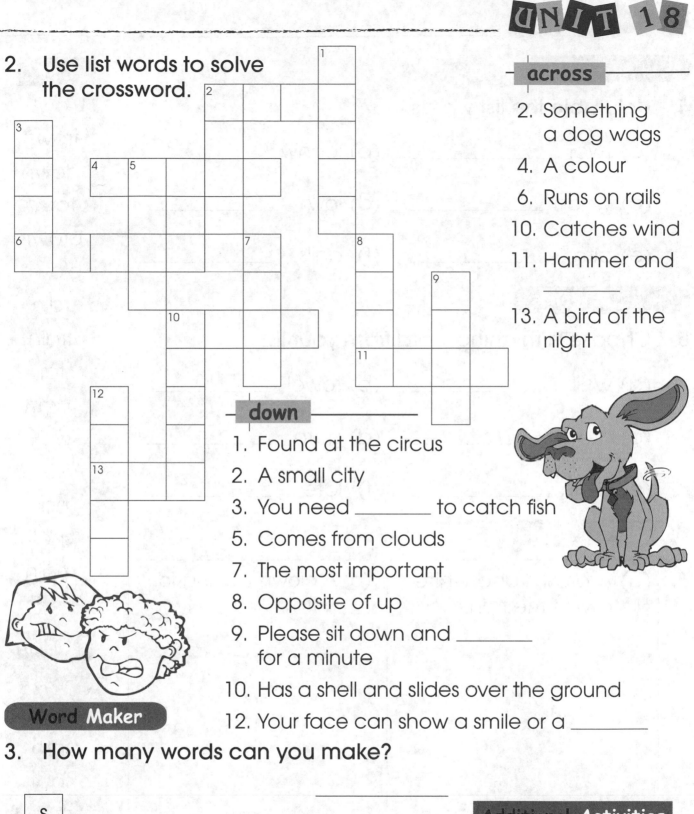

across

2. Something a dog wags
4. A colour
6. Runs on rails
10. Catches wind
11. Hammer and _____
13. A bird of the night

down

1. Found at the circus
2. A small city
3. You need _____ to catch fish
5. Comes from clouds
7. The most important
8. Opposite of up
9. Please sit down and _____ for a minute
10. Has a shell and slides over the ground
12. Your face can show a smile or a _____

Word Maker

3. How many words can you make?

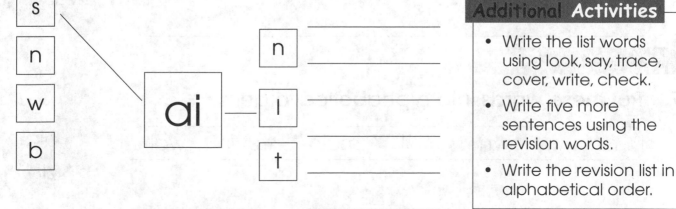

s
n
w
b

ai

n _____
l _____
t _____

_____
_____

Additional Activities

- Write the list words using look, say, trace, cover, write, check.
- Write five more sentences using the revision words.
- Write the revision list in alphabetical order.

All Mixed Up

4. Unjumble the list words.

(a) twai _____   (b) locnw _____

(c) wodn _____   (d) low _____

(e) airn _____   (f) anils _____

Rhyming Words

5. Choose a rhyming word from your list.

(a) wail _____   (b) towel _____

(c) crown _____   (d) gate _____

(e) plain _____   (f) late _____

Read and Draw

6.

(a) A brown and white owl in the rain.	(b) A clown waiting for a train.

Alphabetical Order

7. Put these words into alphabetical order.

| bait   clown   sail   main   frown   wait |

_____

List

owl
frown
down
town
brown
clown
rain
train
tail
bait
wait
sail
nail
snail
main

Revision

yes
boot
into
foot
then
got
ham
took
dig
zip

8. **Find these list words in the word search.**

owl	train
frown	tail
snail	bait
down	wait
town	sail
brown	nail
clown	main
rain	

e	w	a	i	t	r	d	t	f
s	n	a	i	l	a	m	o	r
c	c	d	d	u	i	s	w	o
l	b	r	o	w	n	a	n	w
o	a	e	w	g	q	i	y	n
w	i	u	n	q	g	l	f	d
n	t	j	n	a	i	l	e	o
t	a	i	l	m	a	i	n	w
e	t	r	a	i	n	g	y	l

Word Meanings

9. **Match each word to its meaning.**

    (a) town •   • used to catch fish

    (b) nail •   • found at the end of animals

    (c) tail •   • holds wood together

    (d) bait •   • a small city

Memory Master

10. **Circle the correctly spelled word from the three choices below. Write it from memory.**

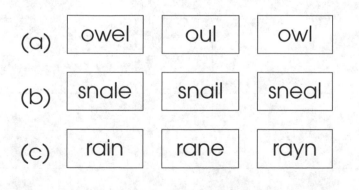

    (a) | owel | oul | owl | _____

    (b) | snale | snail | sneal | _____

    (c) | rain | rane | rayn | _____

Interesting Words from my Writing

Date	Word	Date	Word	Date	Word

Interesting Words from my Writing

Date	Word	Date	Word	Date	Word

My Dictionary Words: Aa to Ii

Aa

Bb

Cc

Dd

Ee

Ff

Gg

Hh

Ii

My Dictionary Words: J j to R r

Jj

Kk

Ll

Mm

Nn

Oo

Pp

Qq

Rr

My Dictionary Words: **S**s to **Z**z

Ss

Tt

Uu

Vv

Ww

Xx

Yy

Zz

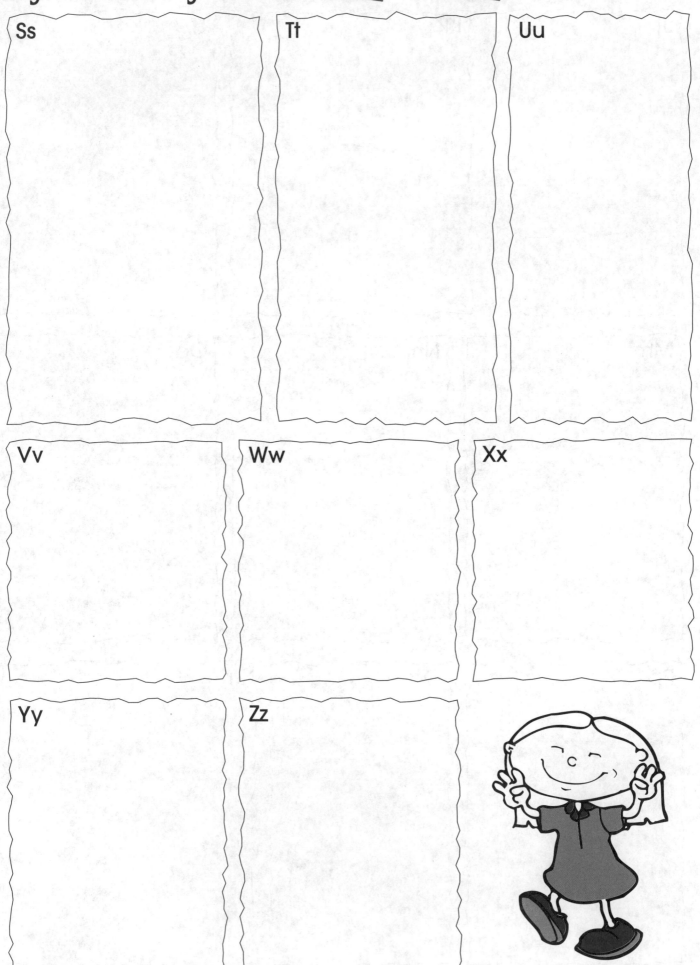